"Fascinating, informative and worthy
of a wide readership in the United States."
—Wernher von Braun
on *The Russian Space Bluff*

The Russian Space Bluff

THE INSIDE STORY OF THE SOVIET DRIVE TO THE MOON

Leonid Vladimirov

Translated from Russian by David Floyd

THE DIAL PRESS   NEW YORK   1973

Library of Congress Cataloging in Publication Data
Vladimirov, Leonid, 1924–
The Russian space bluff.

1. Astronautics—Russia. I. Title.
[WL789.8.R9V5313 1973] 629.4'0947 72–11523

Originally published by Tom Stacey Ltd.,
28/29 Maiden Lane, London WC2E 7JP
Copyright © 1971 by Leonid Vladimirov
Manufactured in the United States of America
First American Printing, 1973

CONTENTS

Foreword by Anatoli Fedoseyev
6

Author's Introduction
10

PART ONE
THE FIRST SPUTNIK
17

PART TWO
'VOSTOK'—THE EAST
The Political Space Race
69

PART THREE
'VOSKHOD'—THE RISING OF THE SUN
Russian Space Technology
121

PART FOUR
THE SETTING OF THE SUN
Research in Fetters
147

Index
189

RUSSIA'S SPACE
LAUNCHING SITES

*Text references are to be
found on the following pages:*

Apartment 23

Nakhabino 25

Special Prison No 4 32

Kratovo 35

*Kaliningrad 43
  (former Podlipki)*

*Sukhumi 43
  (local towns Sinop and
  Agudzera)*

Kapustin Yar 43

Tyuratam 47

Baikonur 47

*Byelorussian Railway
  Station 75*

Dubna 163

Obninsk 164

FOREWORD BY ANATOLI FEDOSEYEV

The greater part of scientific research in the Soviet Union is conducted in such secrecy that it is very difficult for the outsider, and especially the foreigner, to have any clear idea of the level which Soviet science and technology have reached. But space research has by its very nature to be carried on in the open, with the whole world watching. You might think, therefore, that a close study of Soviet achievements in space would provide Western observers with a reliable guide to the present state of Soviet science. This is not the case.

The trouble is that science and technology in the Soviet Union are placed completely at the disposal of the totalitarian state and their advancement is subordinated entirely to the state's political aims. This is not necessarily a bad thing and might conceivably be beneficial if the Soviet state were concerned primarily with achieving the maximum material and spiritual well-being of its people. Unfortunately this is not so. The main objective of the relatively small group of people who rule the Soviet Union today is to hold on to the power they have. If this aim happens to coincide with improving the lot of the Soviet people, well and good. But if it does not coincide, then the people have to suffer.

The nature and direction of space research in the Soviet Union is not determined primarily by scientific considerations but by political and military ones. The main criterion is the extent to which a given piece of research will increase Soviet military potential and raise Soviet prestige in the world. Moreover, despite the

6

teachings of Marx and Lenin—or perhaps because of them—labour productivity is low in the Soviet Union, so that the total resources at the disposal of the government are considerably less than in America. And, although the Soviet leaders have the means of depriving the population of many of the things regarded as essentials in the West, there are strict limits to what they can undertake.

The result of this situation is that decisions on major scientific research projects are often taken quite arbitrarily, seldom on the basis of good scientific reasoning, and often reflect nothing more than the personal prejudices or ambitions of individual leaders. The secrecy in which scientific work is conducted is a further factor contributing to arbitrary decisions. Since nobody but the members of the ruling group themselves has any real idea of what is going on, they are able to embark on any enterprise they please without being required to explain their decisions.

There is another reason for the secrecy, especially as it applies to the leading scientists upon whom the level of science and technology in the Soviet Union really depends. It is not the fear of their being kidnapped which prompts the Soviet authorities to keep them *incognito*. It is rather because, if such people were known to the public they might acquire sufficient fame and influence to represent a powerful and possibly dangerous opposition to the political leaders. The scientists whom the authorities allow to reveal their identities are those who, by virtue of their abilities or characters, are incapable of putting up the slightest opposition. It is a simple matter to get rid of a man who, however important he may be in himself, is unknown inside the Soviet Union and outside it.

The world of Soviet science thus presents a picture utterly at variance with the logic of any Western observer. It fails to correspond in the slightest degree to the practices of any democratic state. No wonder so much of the information received from the Soviet Union simply puzzles the average person in the West. This explains why the theme of Leonid Vladimirov's book was not accepted when he first discussed it a few years ago. It is only in the last few years, during which Soviet space research has made little progress and has suffered the tragic deaths of four astronauts, that most Western observers have begun to have doubts.

It is the great merit of Leonid Vladimirov's book that, for the first time, he provides a complete and convincing explanation of the strange twists and turns of the Soviet space ' programme ' and reveals the sad state of Russian science and technology in the field of space research. For my part I can say that similarly tragic situations exist in the other branches of Soviet science and technology.

The atmosphere which surrounded space research in the Soviet Union and the end to which that bluff has now come do not reflect, of course, on the labours of the many thousands of Soviet scientists and engineers involved. The fate of that great man of science, the designer-engineer Sergei Korolyov, is shared by many other talented and able people in the Soviet Union. In spite of having to work under inhuman pressure and being subjected to the most frightful penalties, these people performed great feats of creative work and made important contributions to their country's science and technology. It was not their fault that the Soviet rulers used their unlimited power to distort and misapply scientific achievements for their own purposes.

I find it difficult to agree with Leonid Vladimirov when he criticises Sergei Korolyov for being ' the great producer of the bluff '. Korolyov was not the man responsible for the bluff. In fact his achievements revealed to the world a vivid picture of a man of great creative ability and character facing up to a régime of meanness and deceit. Another assertion from which I differ is that it became possible to make atomic and hydrogen bombs and atomic submarines in the Soviet Union because of information obtained through espionage and from Pontecorvo. If this were so then the task of countering Soviet military potential would be very simple and cheap to accomplish: it would simply be necessary to increase the secrecy surrounding scientific work in the United States and improve the quality of American counter-intelligence work.

The appearance of atomic weapons in the Soviet Union is certainly not the result of a slip on the part of the American intelligence service. The fact is that the Soviet Union is a totalitarian state which can allot vast resources for the development of new weapons. Moreover, however badly scientific work is organized in the Soviet Union, the number of people is no less in Russia by and large than in other countries, while the total number of scientists and engineers is substantially greater than elsewhere. I consider Mr Vladimirov is mistaken in underestimating the possibilities of the Soviet Union in this connection, particularly if we bear in mind that military technology is priority number one for the Soviet rulers.

As a whole the appearance of this book represents in my view an important event, exposing as it does so fully and so truthfully the essence of the space bluff which was put on by the men who rule the Soviet Union.

18 VIII 1971.

(Anatoli Fedoseyev was a high-ranking Soviet radar scientist before he defected to the West in 1971.)

AUTHOR'S INTRODUCTION

When I left the Soviet Union with the intention of asking for political asylum in Britain I knew for certain that the USSR had quietly abandoned all dreams of engaging in a 'moon race' with the United States and that it would be American and not Soviet spacemen who would be the first to set foot on the Moon. This and a great deal more was perfectly well known, not only to me, but to many of my colleagues—Moscow science writers—not to mention the scientists and other specialists involved in the space flights.

But then I learnt, to my surprise, that everybody in the West believed the reverse to be true. The most extreme optimists, even among the scientists, thought that, even if America were able to overtake the Soviet Union in the race to land on the Moon, it would involve a desperate effort to achieve it. It was apparently this haste and the habit of constantly looking over the shoulder at what was happening in the USSR, which might any day launch a piloted moon-ship, that resulted in the *Apollo* programme being carried out a year sooner than planned, in spite of the disaster which cost the lives of Virgil Grissom and two of his comrades. There can be no doubt that, as a result of its being speeded up, the cost of the whole programme was much greater than expected. But in 1966 and even in 1969 the majority of people in the West were still convinced that no amount of speeding up was going to help the Americans and that the Soviet flag would be flying on the Moon before any of the others.

I was so surprised to find people so ill-informed that I decided immediately to write down everything I knew, so as to reassure some people and no doubt to disappoint others. But it didn't work! Neither I nor my literary agent found it possible to persuade English publishers to take a book which said that the USSR was lagging behind America in space research. After the first unsuccessful attempts I decided to go into the matter with the director of one of London's biggest and most respectable publishing houses. He heard me out, shrugged his shoulders and replied:

'That's very interesting, but all I know is that Russia was first to launch a satellite, first to send a man into space, first to carry out a space flight with more than one man aboard and first to send a spaceman on a walk outside the spaceship. As for the Moon, even there the Russian *Lunik* was the first. Nothing you say can alter these simple facts. And if I now publish your book forecasting that the Americans will win the "moon race" you can imagine what you and I will look like if the Soviet Union wins nevertheless.'

'But that's impossible,' I exclaimed.

The publisher looked at his watch:

'I'm afraid the number of things that are impossible in this world are becoming less and less. But if there is anything impossible then, believe me, it's the publication of your book. At least until we have the answer to the question of who will be first . . .'

I was at the time a very new arrival in the West, so I trusted the experience of my publishing friend and abandoned my intention of writing a book. And then, as was to be expected, there was the launching of *Apollo 11*, followed by *Apollo 12*, the heroic *Apollo 13* and *Apollo 14*. I was of course very sorry that I had not donned the mantle of a prophet, but it was even more painful and strange for me to read the Western press *after* the first three Americans had returned from the Moon. Highly qualified scientific journalists and even serious scholars indulged in all sorts of speculation about what had prevented the Soviet Union at the last moment from overtaking America. The magazine *Aviation Week* printed a brief report about some explosion which was supposed to have taken place at the Soviet 'cosmodrome' at Baikonur. (The joke here was that neither at Baikonur nor anywhere in the neighbourhood of that little Kazakh town was there any 'cosmodrome', and there never had been. Soviet experts in misinformation still manage to mislead many people in the West even on this point.) And many newspapers and magazines proceeded at once to say quite seriously that probably a new super-powerful Soviet rocket had blown up just as it was ready to carry a spaceship to the Moon.

On another occasion I was astonished to read a commentary in the London *Times* about the flight of three Soviet spaceships in October 1969—once again *after* the Americans had already been on the Moon. As we know, nothing new took place in the course of that flight from either the scientific or the technical point of view. But *The Times* wrote in a tone of alarm that the flight of the seven Soviet spacemen in three spaceships undoubtedly signified a revolution in space research—something with which the Russians were about to overshadow all American achievements.

And in 1971, even after the third thoroughly successful American Moon mission, the notion of the Russians still being 'ahead' still prevailed. In April 1971, after launching a 'space station' called 'Salyut' into ordinary circumterrestrial orbit, the USSR sent a spaceship *Soyuz 10* with three aboard to chase it. This kind of flight had nothing new in it because the American astronauts (Neil Armstrong, incidentally,

12

was the first) performed it several times. And yet, this is how the British press treated the event (I quote the *Evening News* of 23 April 1971):

'Two of the *Soyuz 10* crew were believed to be already "setting up home" in *Salyut* to carry out space experiments . . . The Russians have not yet given the names of those in the trio detailed to board *Salyut*, which is also known as the Cosmodom (space-house) . . . They are now *undoubtedly way ahead* of the Americans in the race to build the first permanent platform in space' (Author's emphasis).

Actually nothing of the kind happened that time and the mission appeared to have been a complete failure (though this is not to be admitted by the Russian authorities).

But even if some of the Russian crew managed to climb into the *Salyut* from *Soyuz 10*, there could have been no question of any 'race' and, least of all, of their being 'way ahead' in anything. The reason is simple: if one launches a satellite and then mans it by using another satellite, this is no step forward in the direction of establishing a 'permanent space platform'. Because each time one needs to change the crew or deliver any supply, one must use another spaceship at full cost including the loss of the whole space vehicle. No sooner can a permanent space station be established than one must develop a returnable shuttle to communicate with it. This is precisely what U.S. Space Administration is doing and therefore the first real space platform is scheduled by NASA for 1972-73.

Being aware of this—but unable to develop a shuttle —the Soviets decided to play a trick: to launch a sputnik, man it from another sputnik and call this experiment a 'permanent space station'. Regrettably, with the help of the Western press, some people are only too willing to be deceived.

13

I am writing this while *Salyut* is still circling the Earth—so far empty, due to the failure of the first attempt to man it by *Sayuz 10*. The second attempt— as costly as the first may well be successful and then, I anticipate, there will be a new press barrage of the Russians being 'way ahead' etc.

The most remarkable reaction I came across was an article in a popular French magazine, summing up the results of the 'moon race'. What the article said amounted roughly to the following: the Americans, in their anxiety to overtake the Soviet Union at all costs, had rushed off hysterically (that was the word used) to the Moon, while the Soviet Union had coolly and calmly declined to take part in such an unnecessary performance and had switched resources to the construction of orbital space stations which were far more useful and which would, doubtless, soon be launched into space.

Let us suppose for the moment that the tone of this latter article was influenced by the crude anti-Americanism which is so widespread in France. But neither *The Times* nor *Aviation Week* can be accused of harbouring similar feelings. What, then, is the matter? Why are the judgments of the Western press and even the opinion of certain scientific circles about Soviet space research so catastrophically far from the truth?

The reason is to be found in the colossal and extraordinarily successful game of bluff which the Soviet Union has conducted so cleverly for a good twelve years and which no other country could possibly have got away with. Even today, when the Americans are able to fly to the Moon and back and when many pieces of Soviet space equipment can be compared with the American equipment at international exhibitions, the illusion of the Soviet Union's 'leadership' in space has still been scarcely disturbed. I shall be happy if this book helps a few minds to be liberated from this state of hypnosis.

That does not mean that the reader should expect to find anything 'anti-Russian' in this book. On the contrary, the knowledge I have of the conditions in which space research had its origins in the USSR fills me with admiration for the people who succeeded in the face of unimaginable difficulties and at the risk of their lives to reach the point of actual space launchings. Many of those people were known to me personally, and about others I have a great deal of information. Practically all of them are distinguished by their exceptional ability as engineers and their unlimited devotion to their work. Moreover, the father of Soviet space flight, Sergei Pavlovich Korolyov was, beyond any doubt, a genius and a fanatic in the best sense of that word.

Unfortunately the talent and enthusiasm of brilliant scientists and technicians are exploited by the Soviet dictatorship for purposes which have very little to do with the interests of science or humanity. A great many scientific experts are fully aware of this, but they know very well that there is nothing they can do about it. As we shall soon see, Korolyov himself was very deeply affected by this tragic situation. But even he, who had direct access to Khrushchev at any time, had favours showered on him and was considered to be all-powerful, was utterly helpless to change the situation although he tried to do so in the last years of his life.

The principal weapon which made it possible for the Soviet Union to play its game of cosmic bluff was, and remains, the all-pervading secrecy under cover of which all scientific work of any significance at all is conducted in the USSR. This secrecy is ensured by the fact that for 'disclosing a State or military secret' any person, irrespective of the position he holds, is sent to a prison camp for eight years. That is the sentence if the 'secret' is disclosed because the person is careless or too talkative. If the secret information is passed to somebody intentionally the punishment will be far more severe—up to and including the death sentence. For this reason I am, unfortunately, unable to mention in my book all my sources, because if I did those same sources, still living and working in the repressive atmosphere of the Soviet Union, would immediately suffer reprisals. I shall have to change deliberately the names of places where things take place and of the jobs and even names of people so as not to put the secret police on the track of people who trusted me with information.

I must, however, point out that I do not have at my disposal any technical information which would amount to a military or even a commercial secret in the Soviet Union—nothing which in the West would come under the heading of secret information. My friends among the scientists and technicians who were working in the field of space research never spoke of such things and I never bothered to enquire. But you will realise in the course of reading this book that the Soviet authorities consider it important to maintain secrecy, not only about plans, patents and inventions, but also about conditions of work, particular events and, most important, their own technical backwardness. Every Soviet technician and science writer knows more than enough of such 'secrets'. And I am, as it happens, both an engineer and a scientific journalist who worked in direct contact with Soviet space experts for more than six years—from 1960 to 1966.

After this unavoidable introduction I can start to tell the story of why there are and could be no Soviet spacemen on the Moon.

Leonid Vladimirov
1971

PART ONE

THE FIRST SPUTNIK

In the late autumn of 1965 the Moscow writer Anatoli Markusha, a former military pilot who, despite his Jewish origins, had been awarded the highest decorations, submitted to the editor of the magazine I was working on, a short story called 'The Birthday'. We read the manuscript, scarcely able to believe our eyes. It was the story of how the government had decided to reveal the name of the mysterious Chief Designer of spaceships and how, on his birthday, to his own great surprise the newspaper had published huge pictures of him along with messages of congratulation from the country's top leaders and even the official *ukaze* concerning another award. There was not the slightest doubt that the person the author had in mind was Korolyov—whose name was at the time absolutely unknown to people in the Soviet Union—because the story gave precise biographical details, including a reference to Korolyov's period of detention in prison.

As I recall, we wanted to hand the story straight back to the author. It was useless in our view even to try to publish it—it would never get through the censor. But Markusha insisted to an extent unusual in such a modest person. 'Go on—have a try. It

17

won't cost you anything! Let it get at least as far as the censor. It's really very important.'

We did not see very clearly why it was important, but we tried nonetheless. The story reached the censor all right, and he immediately banned its publication. But very soon afterwards the main event in the story—the publication of the picture and name of Korolyov—came about unexpectedly and in the most unhappy way. His picture and his name were indeed published in the middle of January 1966, on the occasion, not of his birthday, but of his death.

Even then, after the death of the great rocket scientist who had been responsible for sending into space the first artificial satellite, the first living creature and the first man, the authorities would not permit us to say who he actually was and what he had done. The press referred only to the death of Academician Sergei Pavlovich Korolyov—'a major specialist in the field of mechanics'. It was only several months later, after pressure had been applied by scientists who wanted to pay due homage to Korolyov's memory and, perhaps, have their own names published too, that permission was given for it to be stated, but without any special fuss, that Korolyov and the mystical Chief Designer, about whom 'trusted' journalists had been writing in fanciful terms since 1957, were one and the same person.

The ban on reference to Korolyov's name has now been removed. Numerous reminiscences about him and even an official biography—the book *Academician Korolyov*—have appeared. But there are more gaps in this literature than there are true facts, and the position of the remaining and still surviving space experts in the USSR has not changed in any way: their names are still kept secret, they are not permitted to travel abroad or even to meet foreigners at home in Russia, and at international congresses on space matters—

at the KOSPAR congresses, for example—their places are taken by figure-heads such as Academicians Sedov and Blagonravov.

At the same time I have proof that Korolyov in his lifetime more than once protested against the anonymity in which he was kept. He repeatedly begged Khrushchev and later his successors to allow the names of the men who had created the space machines to be published. Korolyov was particularly enraged by an affair involving Academician Sedov. Shortly after the launching of the first sputnik, in their determination to mislead world public opinion, the Soviet authorities decided to put forward Academician Sedov as one of the main figures in Soviet space launchings. This was not done straightforwardly, however, but in the sort of roundabout way typical of the Soviet leaders.

When Sedov travelled abroad to some congress or other the rumour was put around very cautiously to the effect that he, Sedov, was in fact the Chief Designer. People naturally besieged him with questions, and he, as he had been ordered, gave neither a flat denial of them nor any direct confirmation. The Soviet papers wrote on that occasion: 'The Soviet delegation to the congress attracted great attention, especially Academician L. I. Sedov, whom the Western press describes as the father of the first sputnik'.

It is said that Korolyov, furious at this statement, immediately demanded to see Khrushchev and threatened to go into retirement if the authorities insisted on putting up a puppet in his place. The Chief Designer also insisted on the publication of the names of all the people decorated by the government for their part in launching the first sputnik. Khruschhev did not dare to punish the recalcitrant designer, but decided to compromise: the names of the scientists were not published, but all references to Sedov as the author of the sputnik were stopped once and for all.

It is possible that it was this exchange which produced the first crack in relations between Khrushchev and Korolyov. From then on those relations were invariably cool. But Khrushchev, crafty and cynical, had an excellent device for keeping Korolyov on a tight rein without having to resort to force as Stalin had done in his day. What that device was will emerge from later chapters.

As for Korolyov's relations with Brezhnev and Kosygin, who divided Khrushchev's duties between themselves after the October palace revolution of 1964, they did not in fact ever have time to take shape. Korolyov died fourteen months and two weeks after Brezhnev and Kosygin seized power. There can be no doubt, however, that he began to hope for some improvement. He began to persuade the new rulers to change Soviet 'space policy' in the direction of greater publicity, to increase scientific exchanges and to reveal the names of the 'hidden' Soviet scientists.

Shortly after Brezhnev and Kosygin took power they received a detailed report by Korolyov on the current state of space research, both in the Soviet Union and in the United States. Korolyov was extremely frank. He said straight out that Soviet space research had not been conducted so far according to any scientific programme but on the principle of 'beat the Americans at all costs', and that it would not be possible to stick to that principle much longer because the United States were far ahead in terms both of rocket motors and of electronic equipment. Korolyov explained to Brezhnev and Kosygin—both men with some technical education—the methods which had been used at Khrushchev's insistence to overtake the American *Gemini* programme, and it is said that the two Soviet leaders were shocked. (I shall describe those methods in detail later.) Korolyov said that

20

it might be possible to release a man from a space-craft while in space sooner than the Americans planned to do it, but that the next stage in the *Gemini* programme —the docking of two space-craft while in orbit—was beyond the capacity of the Soviet Union for at least the next three or four years. The Chief Designer invited his new masters to inspect the completed three-man craft *Soyuz* which could not, however, be launched because of the absence of a sufficiently powerful and reliable rocket booster. Korolyov ended by saying that they would have to abandon all dreams of putting people on the Moon sooner than the Americans, and that instead they should draw up their own programme of space research and act on it.

There is good reason to believe that Korolyov's report had some effect. At the beginning of 1965, we science writers were given secret instructions to make no further reference whatsoever to the coming conquest of the Moon by the Soviet Union. If you study the Soviet press for that period you will find that up to the very end of 1964—even in the last months of 1964 when Nikita Khrushchev had already been swept off his throne—frequent passages to the effect that 'that time is not far off when the Soviet flag will be flying on the Moon' and so forth. But then, from the beginning of 1965, all such boastful talk ceased. It was then, when we received those instructions, that we realised immediately that it had been decided to 'yield' first place in the 'moon race' to the Americans, and it was not long before I discovered from talks with Korolyov's colleagues what underlay the decision.

The second consequence of Korolyov's report was —for me at least—Anatoli Markusha's short story 'The Birthday' which I mentioned at the beginning of this chapter. Markusha insisted that the story should at least get as far as the censor, and he had his own good reasons for insisting. He was an old acquaintance of Korolyov's and the Chief Designer had undoubtedly inspired that 'trial balloon' in the hope that the top leaders would understand at last how stupid it was to praise anonymous scientists.

I know too that a member of the staff of *Pravda* who had prepared an article by Korolyov for publication (the Chief Designer occasionally wrote in *Pravda* under the pseudonym 'Konstantinov') was rather surprised when, as he checked the final version of the article, Korolyov, stern and unbelievably busy, suddenly let out: 'Next time maybe I'll sign it with my own name.' The journalist did not take it upon himself to ask questions but simply related the unusual incident to me in confidence.

Sad to relate, Korolyov never signed with his own name any article written after the sputnik was launched. He was allotted the same fate as that of H. G. Wells's 'invisible man'—eventually to become visible only after his death, and that not immediately. Unless there are changes in the USSR the same fate awaits Korolyov's colleagues.

From all the information which I have at my disposal, however, Sergei Pavlovich Korolyov should not be regarded as an unhappy man. He was, after all, one of the very few members of the human race who succeeded in seeing and touching with his hands the realisation of his whole life's dream. My grounds for saying this are not to be found in the official biographies which, of course, declare Korolyov to have been an inspired dreamer about rockets from his early childhood. I base it rather on a pamphlet called *Rocket Motors* written by Korolyov and published by the Soviet military publishers in *1932*—a quarter of a century before the first sputnik. That pamphlet was written by a 25-year-old enthusiast hardly out of college.

At the time Sergei Korolyov was already a member of the so-called 'Group for the Study of Rocket Motion' (known by its Russia initials as GIRD), a body formed without official support by a German from Riga called Friedrich Zander, which did its work in the basement of a block of flats in Moscow. Zander was an unrestrained fanatic on the question of rockets: he knew by heart everything that had been written by Goddard and Oberth, was striving to repeat their achievements and launch at least one rocket of his own. In the last year of his life (1933), he succeeded in his aim. The first Soviet rocket reached a height of 1,300 feet. Three months later a second rocket was launched, but Zander was no longer alive to see it.

What exactly Friedrich Zander died of, at the early age of 46, I do not know. Officially, he was said to have died of tuberculosis; less official sources said he died from malnutrition. (There was a cruel famine in Russia at the time.) According to completely unofficial sources—from muffled hints dropped by the few surviving members of GIRD—he was 'liquidated' by the secret police for his alleged connection with members of the 'industrial party'—that is, with the group of scientists who had a short time previously been condemned for 'sabotage' without the slightest evidence of their guilt being produced. At all events the Soviet encyclopaedia on space research published in 1969 gives no reason for Zander's premature death, while in the *Academician Korolyov* he simply disappears from the story at a certain point without any indication being given of when he died.

But one thing is certain: that Friedrich Zander succeeded in infecting some of the other people working in GIRD with that tremendous enthusiasm—the 'rocket mania' which remained with many of them, including Korolyov, for the rest of their lives. One incident is sufficient to illustrate the attitude of members of the staff of GIRD to their work. In the course of constructing the first rocket they found they needed

23

some silver solder to join some wires, but it was un-thinkable at the time that they should be able to get their hands on some silver. Nevertheless, one of the engineers employed by GIRD secretly brought from his home a silver teaspoon which they melted down and used for the joint. The man had to bring it secretly, not because he was afraid of upsetting his wife, but because all precious metals were supposed to be handed over to the State, and the GPU, as the secret police was then called, used to subject anyone suspected of hiding gold or silver to what was known as the 'pumping out' process. They would simply arrest a person and hold him in prison until such time as he told them where his valuables were hidden. A dozen silver spoons did not, of course, constitute a major crime, but if someone had reported that he had taken silver from his house he could well have been arrested the next day for 'pumping out'. The people employed in GIRD received no money for their work: they had to earn their living elsewhere. But they did not count on receiving any reward for their efforts and used to say that the letters GIRD stood in fact for 'Group of Engineers Working for Nothing'.

It was at that time that Korolyov revealed for the first time another very important talent—his capacity for diplomacy. He was very skilful in his approach to the people in power and he knew how to present the course and results of his work in such a way that his bosses felt themselves convinced of the importance of the problems he was dealing with. Moreover, Korolyov developed his relations with people in high places in such a way that the initiative appeared to come from them and not from him: he appeared only to be carrying out the tasks with which he had been entrusted.

This was not, of course, a new tactic; it is centuries old. But in the Soviet Union, where everything depends on the word of some highly placed ignoramus, it was

24

the only path to success. And Korolyov cannot be accused of dishonesty in this connection, because he was not seeking any advantages for himself. He wanted only one thing: to have the possibility of building and launching rockets, which were regarded at the time as a sort of plaything, useless and sometimes dangerous.

In fact the first highly placed leader whom Korolyov succeeded in interesting in rockets was anything but an ignoramus. He managed to have access to the Deputy People's Commissar for military and naval matters, Mikhail Tukhachevsky, a highly educated officer of the regular army and a very intelligent man. Tukhachevsky had distinguished himself in his day by the ferocity with which he had dealt with the sailors of Kronstadt when they rose in rebellion in 1921. But in the thirties he was doing serious work on re-equipping the army and took under his wing authors of inventions having some military value. Korolyov's choice was thus very fortunate; he was not to know that four years later Tukhachevsky would be executed as a 'German spy' and that all the people he had protected would also be destroyed or sent to a prison camp.

In his talk with Tukhachevsky, Korolyov insisted, of course, on the possibility of using rockets for military purposes. (They were, incidentally, used for such purposes even by the ancient Egyptians.) And he succeeded in arousing Tukhachevsky's interest. A letter from him has been preserved in which he says that the work of GIRD 'is of considerable importance for the military departments and for the USSR as a whole'. Those were indeed prophetic words, inspired by Sergei Korolyov.

With Tukhachevsky's help, GIRD obtained the use of a small launching base at the military engineering centre at Nakhabino near Moscow. It was there in fact that the launching of the Soviet Union's first-ever rocket took place—it weighed 38 pounds, rose to a height of 1,300 feet and remained airborne for 18 seconds. The launching of that rocket undoubtedly cost Sergei Korolyov far greater effort than the launching of the first sputnik 24 years later.

Korolyov's official Soviet biographer, P. Astashenkov, described the situation in the *Moscow* magazine (No. 11 for 1969): 'In this way, by turning for help to the most influential people, Sergei Pavlovich fought to obtain each lathe, each bench and each tool'. Korolyov had to resort to the most unusual devices and to appeal to such qualities in the people at the top as were by no means obvious at the time. For example, very few people, even in the Soviet Union, know the story of the 'second birth' of Konstantin Tsiolkovsky.

Tsiolkovsky was an inventor—a self-educated man of Polish origin. At the time he was a very old man, living in Kaluga, about 110 miles from Moscow, forgotten by everybody. After the revolution he had nearly died of starvation but he had eventually managed to obtain a minute pension. But way back in 1903 Tsiolkovsky had published at his own expense a pamphlet entitled *Research into inter-planetary space by means of Jet Power*, in which he had discussed, among other things, the possibility of using liquid-fuel and multi-stage rockets. He later abandoned these problems and was taken up with designing a rigid airship and then a high-speed train. In the mid-twenties, however, when he heard about the successful rocket launchings by Goddard and Oberth, Tsiolkovsky returned to the question of rockets, in an article entitled *An Inter-Planetary Ship* and sent it to the magazine *Technology and Life*. It was not published at the time and finally saw the light of day only in 1961.

So Zander and Korolyov, knowing what had happened to Tsiolkovsky, decided to bring him back to life, so to speak. A memorandum was sent to the Politburo of the Central Committee of the Communist

Party reporting that the man said to be the instigator of rocket science and of the future interplanetary flights was still alive in the Soviet Union. It was suggested that it would be a good idea to show the world the way the Soviet régime cared about the future of humanity and at the same time sing the praises of another Russian genius. (Nowhere, not in a single Soviet work on Tsiolkovsky, not even in the long biography written by the very able author M. Arlazorov, is there any reference to the fact that Tsiolkovsky was a Pole.)

The memorandum had its effect, and the whole Soviet propaganda machine swung into action with much noise. They brought Tsiolkovsky, deaf and ailing, to Moscow and made him, with the aid of a hearing trumpet, listen to endless speeches and give interviews on every conceivable question, far beyond the limits of space research. Articles were written about Tsiolkovsky's work such as were not written 25 years later even about the Chief Designer of the space-craft. Carried away by their enthusiasm, readers of the newspapers of the time sent in tearful letters begging the great Tsiolkovsky to send them to the Moon or to Mars in the first Soviet space craft.

The people from GIRD met Tsiolkovsky, quickly explained to him the point of what was going on, and from that day until his death in 1935 Tsiolkovsky was an important—and a very effective—supporter of everything in the field of rocketry. Korolyov for his part took care to see that interest in Tsiolkovsky did not dwindle. A whole institute was set up in Moscow under the name of a 'Commission for the development of the ideas of K. E. Tsiolkovsky'. Dozens of articles and books were written about his ideas and the possibility of putting them into practice. I remember how, as a boy of ten, I enjoyed reading a popular children's book on the same subject, written by J. I. Perelman, who was at the time the best writer on scientific themes for the general public. It must be added that in those days, unlike the present situation, it was possible to give the names of foreign researchers as well as of Soviet ones. And, to do Perelman justice, it has to be said that he mentioned both Goddard and Oberth. He described the rockets they had launched and glossed skilfully over the fact that Tsiolkovsky (to whom the book was in the main devoted) had not launched a single rocket throughout his whole life. It was much later that I learnt that Korolyov was friendly with J. I. Perelman and put the idea of such a book into his head. This is now confirmed by statements in the Korolyov biography.

The tremendous energy which the young designer put into his work was crowned with a very important success: on 31 October 1933 a Government decree was published providing for the amalgamation of GIRD with the Leningrad Laboratory of Gas Dynamics (GDL) and the formation on this basis of an Institute for Research into Jet Propulsion. This was an event of tremendous significance in Soviet scientific life: from being merely a group of 'pretenders', of amateur and rather suspect enthusiasts, GIRD became a State institution and a part of the military establishment to boot. It was immediately provided with a full staff of employees, high salary scales and even military ranks. To understand the extent of the sudden change that came over the situation of the 'Group of Scientists Working for Nothing' it is sufficient to cite the example of Korolyov himself. Upon being appointed on 9 November 1933 to the post of deputy head of the institute, he was immediately given the title of divisional engineer, which was equivalent to the rank of general!

But it became clear at once that Korolyov had no intention of becoming an administrator, of sitting in an office and wearing a general's uniform. It was not for the sake of a career that he had fought for the setting up of the institute. To the amazement of his superiors and colleagues, Korolyov removed the badges of ranks from his tunic and turned down the office and secretary that were offered him. He became completely absorbed in the design of two machines at the same time—a rocket and a glider equipped with a liquid-fuel jet motor. The rocket, which was intended to have a flight range of 30 miles, became airborne on only two occasions, and both flights were unfortunately unsuccessful. The glider equipped with a jet auxiliary engine made its first flight only in 1940, but Korolyov was not present at the test because by then he was behind bars.

Behind Bars

It must be said that Sergei Korolyov was incredibly, fantastically lucky. Literally every one of the people of any importance who had worked at the jet propulsion institute were executed in 1937 or 1938. In that blood-bath of executions people incomparably more successful and better known than Korolyov at the time were destroyed. There was, for example, another deputy head of the same institute, the inventor of the Soviet rocket artillery which came to be known in the war years as *Katushas*—Georgi Langemak. Langemak was executed along with the whole of his group of designers with the exception of one engineer—A. G. Kostikov. It was under the guidance of this Kostikov that the manufacture of Langemak's *Katushas* went ahead. When war broke out in 1941 and the *Katushas* turned out to be an effective weapon, Kostikov was given the highest awards, and then executed like the others.

In this way the overwhelming majority of the members of the staff of the jet-propulsion institute, including its head, Ivan Kleimenov and his deputy,

Georgi Langemak, were executed, but Sergei Korolyov was only arrested. What was the reason for this?

While still in Moscow I heard a lot of talk on this subject. People who had not liked Korolyov and had been jealous of him (and such people included, strange though it may seem, one of the former members of the same institute, a man older than Korolyov and one who, like Korolyov, escaped execution) cast vague accusations in his direction. They implied that Korolyov had been due to be among the first to die because he had been more closely linked than any of them with Tukhachevsky and that after July 1937, when Tukhachevsky and the other top military leaders were unexpectedly executed, the name 'Tukhachevsky' had become a synonym for death. And if Korolyov was not among the first to die—according to these people—if he managed to get away with being arrested and spent only six years in relatively comfortable detention, then there must be something fishy about it —perhaps he had collaborated with the security police and betrayed other people.

I am not disposed to put any faith in such doubtful exercises in deduction. Shakespeare's 'Though this be madness, yet there is method in it' does not apply to an analysis of Stalin's terror in 1937 and 1938. They were years during which the ruler acted in an utterly arbitrary manner, such as had no parallel in history, and a man's life was determined by a chain of the most unlikely, apparently disconnected, events. It is a known fact that after the most frightful plague epidemics there were always some people left who had lived through the whole epidemic in the most dangerous place, been in contact with hundreds of sick people and had still not caught the illness themselves. The author of these lines himself spent slightly less time than Korolyov in prisons and prison camps and knows from his own experience how sometimes pure chance could lead to a man's death and how equally unlikely coincidences could save another's life.

But, apart from these general considerations, I have a sort of explanation of the happy fact that Korolyov was not executed. The fact is that in his student years he worked under the guidance of Andrei Tupolev, the man who later was to be responsible for developing numerous Soviet aircraft of the ANT and TU types. When in 1938 Tupolev, along with his wife and all his leading engineers (again with one exception!), were put into the Butyrki prison, this started a hunt for 'Tupolev's boys'—his former colleagues, pupils and friends. Every time a major figure such as Tupolev was arrested the NKVD (as the secret police was then called) made every effort to 'expose a plot with extensive ramifications'. Korolyov was in fact arrested as one of Tupolev's associates and it was that which saved his life, because at a certain point Stalin gave orders that Tupolev's people were not to be executed but put to work. In this way Korolyov—for the second time and this time against his wishes—went to work for Tupolev. He did the wing calculations in the 'TKB'—the Prison Design Office—attached to aircraft factory No. 156.

With the outbreak of war, factory No. 156 was evacuated to the Siberian town of Omsk, and the designers who were also prisoners were sent there along with the factory. In Omsk the prison regime was relaxed to some extent, and Tupolev himself lived in a separate house which he had no right to leave, however, without special permission. After the new dive-bomber the TU-2 appeared at the front and gave a good account of itself, Tupolev and his engineers were pardoned and simply went on working in the same design bureau, but as normal citizens

31

enjoying all their rights. Shortly afterwards they were transferred back to Moscow.

Korolyov had, however, been removed from Omsk even earlier. He was transported as an ordinary prisoner to Moscow, where he was put into 'Special Prison No. 4'.

Today, Alexander Solzhenitsyn's book *The First Circle* is well known in the West. It describes, in a literary manner, one of Stalin's most revolting inventions —special prisons for scientists and engineers. Had it not been for the appearance of *The First Circle* many people might not have believed what I say—after all, I myself was never in a special prison. But, from numerous conversations with former special prisoners I know all the details about such prisons, including prison No. 4 on the outskirts of Moscow in a street which, ironically enough, is called 'Enthusiasts' Road'.

The building which houses the prison is cut off from the outside world by a high wall and stands back from the main road next to a gas-works. Inside are designing rooms, laboratories and living quarters. Everybody, prisoners and warders alike, is dressed in denim trousers and jackets. They work twelve hours a day and sometimes longer (after the war ended the official working day in special prisons was reduced to nine hours). The prisoners are allowed to speak to each other only about their work. They receive three meals a day in a common canteen, and the quality and quantity of the food is not to be compared with a prison or prison camp diet—there is more of it, it is better prepared and more appetising—although, on the other hand, it is a great deal worse than, say, prison diet in Britain. The prisoners' accommodation varies according to their 'rank'—the hierarchical structure of Soviet society being maintained even in prison. The most 'important' prisoners have separate rooms, some of the others live three or four to a room, and others have to live in large dormitories. Nevertheless, every prisoner has his own bed and does not have to sleep on the sort of two-tier bunks used in prison camps or on wooden shelves, as in prison. There is a library containing works of fiction and a shop where the prisoners can buy extra food, soap and various brands of cigarettes for the money they have earned or had sent them.

But in some respects life in a special prison was worse than in a prison camp. For example, in their free time the occupants of the different rooms (the word 'cell' was not used there) were forbidden to communicate with one another. Visits from relatives were permitted only once every three months, and for these meetings the prisoners were transported to the Taganka prison and were forbidden, under threat of having another eight years added to their sentence, to tell their relatives where they were actually living and working. There were severe restrictions on their right to send letters or receive them.

Such were the conditions in which some of the best representatives of the Soviet technical intelligentsia were expected to exercise their creative abilities and strengthen further the political system which, without their having committed any crime against it, had put them into prison. And how they worked! Among Korolyov's predecessors in the prison had been one of Russia's leading experts on power plants, Professor Ramzin, along with his colleagues, including Professor Shumsky, whose lectures on the theory of power plants I myself used to attend. While he was in prison, Ramzin invented what was at the time the most advanced form of boiler—the direct circulation system. After that even Stalin decided to take pity on Leonid Ramzin and set him free. He died shortly after.

In the prison Korolyov found himself among people he already knew well, because a group of designers had already been selected for him from among the old rocket scientists who had survived. I say 'old' although at the time when he was transferred to the prison Korolyov was only 36 and most of his subordinates were even younger. One of the ablest people among them was L. A. Voskresensky who later became Korolyov's deputy in work on the sputniks and piloted space-craft. At that time Voskresensky was only just 30 but was already regarded as an 'old lag'. Voskresensky died at the age of 52 in 1965, a year sooner than Korolyov—prison life does not exactly promote longevity. He was given an elaborate funeral at the governmental cemetery at the Novodevichy monastery in Moscow, but without a single word being written to say exactly who he was. Even today the name of Voskresensky means nothing at all to the average Soviet citizen, who would be very surprised to learn that Korolyov himself declared at Voskresensky's graveside: 'Had it not been for the brain and the talent of this man we would never have launched the sputnik before the Americans.'

Korolyov's new prison design bureau started to work on the development of jet engines for military aircraft then in production. The idea was that such engines fitted under the wings or tail of fighters or bombers would be able to produce a substantial increase in the aircraft's speed when needed and also reduce the length of run required for take-off. The idea of using jet engines to supplement piston engines was not followed up later, but it was very fashionable at the time. Korolyov turned the special prison into an enormous workshop in which he constructed models of engines which were complete right down to the last screw. But he told the people in charge that all the work he was doing would be absolutely useless unless he was allowed to leave the prison to take part in testing the engines. Only if he were able to observe the behaviour of the engine in flight would he be able to create a viable production version. In the end, Korolyov was permitted to do this and proceeded to make trips, escorted by an officer of the security police, to Kratovo near Moscow, where Vasilchenko, the test-pilot, put the engine through its paces in the air.

The Soviet press published one extremely valuable report of a meeting with Korolyov at the test aerodrome when he was still a prisoner. The note-books of the famous Soviet pilot Mark Gallai were published first in the review *Novy Mir* (No. 4 for 1963) and later as a separate book under the title *Tested in the Sky*. The author relates how on one occasion 'while we were still at war' (which means towards the end of the war) he arrived at an aerodrome and saw in the air an aircraft 'with a roaring flame bursting out of its tail'. Gallai began to ask people what had happened—'I don't like seeing flames on an aircraft,' he wrote. It was explained to him that there was nothing amiss, that Vasilchenko was testing a liquid-fuel jet engine.

The plane with the fiery tail landed safely, and Vasilchenko then introduced the designer of the engine to Gallai. I will quote his words: ' "And here is the designer," Vasilchenko replied and pointed out to me a thick-set man of medium height wearing clothes that appeared rather strange, especially for the summer—a jacket and trousers made of the sort of black satin that is used for linings.

'In a flash I recognised who he was. We had been introduced several years before the war but we had not met again since then, through no fault of ours. Nevertheless I had a very good idea of the sort of man he was. I had got to know most about him from accounts given by my friend, the test-pilot V. P. Fyodorov, who had done a lot of work with this designer and in particular had tested his 'rocket-glider' which I have already written about in my first book. Fyodorov spoke of him in very warm, friendly tones, with

tremendous respect and unconcealed pain at the difficult life he had had.

'I went up to the designer, we shook hands, moved
away a little and sat down on some wooden beams which
were lying by the aerodrome fence.

'Throughout the unhurried conversation which followed a lieutenant whom I did not know kept fussing
around us in an agitated manner like a dog on a lead.
At one moment he would be sitting down beside us,
then he would jump up again, then sit down again,
trying his utmost not to miss a single word that passed
between us. Altogether it appeared as though the
poor fellow had the feeling that something improper
was going on, but he couldn't find any good excuse for
interfering, because I obviously did not come under
the heading of 'not having any connection'. I made
myself as inaccessible as I could, assuming for perhaps
the first time in my life all the importance due to my
major's rank, and in any case our conversation did
not touch on anything that went beyond narrowly
professional matters directly concerned with the
aircraft being tested. Not on the surface, at least. As
for the unspoken content of our conversation, there
were no instructions how to deal with that.

'To a bystander the whole of this scene probably
looked rather comic, but at that moment, by contrast
with my usual state of mind, I seemed to have lost
completely the ability to appreciate the funny side of
things.

'I saw standing before me something different: yet
another way (and how many more are there of them?)
in which man's inflexible courage can be demonstrated.
Through the medium of the utterly prosaic words about
thrust and fuel consumption and the number of
repeated ignitions I was able to appreciate fully the
inner character of a man whose creative powers had
been directed throughout his life in one clearly defined

direction, which he had followed in the face of all kinds of obstacles and with manifest contempt (at least on the surface) for all the setbacks which an unkind fate had heaped upon him.

'Before me was sitting the real Chief Designer, just the same as he was when he became famous fifteen or so years later—energetic and far-sighted, intelligent and impatient, brusque yet receptive, quickly aroused, yet soon appeased. He was a big man, with a big complex, contradictory and very unusual character which could not be deformed by any external circumstances such as have broken many people like reeds . . .'

To dispose of any lingering doubts which might remain as to whether Gallai was actually talking about Korolyov and at the same time to fix more precisely the date when the designer was arrested, it remains for me only to quote a passage from the official Soviet biography of Korolyov, published in 1969:

'In 1939—on 29 January and 8 March—two flights took place of rocket *212*. The designer himself was not present at these test flights *for reasons beyond his control* (my emphasis-L.V.). The test flights of the rocket-glider, which he had been planning for many long years, also took place without Korolyov being present. This work was entrusted to Vladimir Fyodorov, one of the best aircraft and glider pilots of the time.'

As you can see, there can be no doubt about it. It is almost incredible that the episode described in M. Gallai's memoirs, which reveal at once just how inaccurate the official biographies of Korolyov are, should have passed through the Soviet censorship and been published in magazines and books. But it happened, and I even know how it came about.

It is clear from his memoirs that Gallai was friendly with Korolyov, and it is highly unlikely that, when he was working on his reminiscences in 1962, the famous test-pilot included the prison episode without the knowledge of the principal character involved. Of course he asked Korolyov about it. And we already know what Korolyov's attitude was to the anonymity in which he was kept and how he had tried to break through the wall of silence. Just as later, in the case of Anatoli Markusha's short story, Korolyov agreed that Gallai should try and slip the important episode into his book.

The manuscript of the book *Tested in the Sky* had, according to the system in the Soviet Union, to pass through a double censorship—first the military and then the general, political censorship. The military censor was an acquaintance of mine, an air-force colonel by the name of Likarenko, who dealt with questions of aviation technology in the Military Censor's Office of the Armed Forces of the USSR. Of course, he immediately noticed the 'dangerous' episode, spoke to the author about it and gathered from what he said that 'the man himself' wanted the episode to be published. If Likarenko were now living I would not dare to recount such stories about him. But this intelligent and rather sad person, with his long, dark moustache, who was in many respects a very remarkable character, died after I emigrated from the Soviet Union. Even in such rigid institutions as the Military Censorship there are a few decent and reasonable people.

However, it would not have been enough for Likarenko simply to put his stamp of approval on the manuscript. The military censor makes only a superficial study of a manuscript and authorises the publication only of special information of a military nature. The manuscript is then passed to the censor in Glavlit, the political censorship, where the final decision is taken as to whether it can be published. The text of the military censor's approval which is stamped on the manuscript and which I frequently had stamped on

articles for the magazine I worked on reads as follows:
'There are no objections to the publication of the
information of a military character contained in this
manuscript. The final decision about its suitability
for publication must be taken by the authorities in
Glavlit.' Which means that even if Colonel Likarenko
had done no more than put his stamp and signature
on it the censor at Glavlit would almost certainly have
cut out the doubtful passage.

But Likarenko acted in a far more subtle manner.
In the course of checking a given text the military
censor has the right to make corrections and comments
and to strike out passages—'if such action is for the
purpose of preserving a military secret'. The military
censor's formal approval, the text of which I have
quoted above, also contains the sentence: 'See our
comments on pages . . .' The passages which have
been checked and corrected by the military are, of
course, subject to the same censorship by Glavlit
as the rest of the text. But the situation is psychologically
rather different. If the Glavlit censor sees in a certain
passage traces of the work of his military colleague he
is inclined to assume that there is nothing to bother
about because the military censor will have amended
the text in accordance with the demands of the censorship. The Glavlit censor practically always lets such
passages through without making any changes.

Very well aware of all this, Likarenko 'worked over'
the section dealing with Gallai's meeting with Korolyov
as a prisoner, cut out a few quite unimportant words and
wrote his initials in the margin. And it worked!
Whether the censor at Glavlit simply overlooked the
'dangerous' passage or whether he simply put his
faith in the authority of the highly experienced Likarenko, the fact is that the passage was published, with
the result that the whole world can now confirm the
fact that the Chief Designer of space-craft, creator of

the first Soviet sputniks, Academician, recipient of every possible prize, whether named for Stalin or Lenin, a Hero of Socialist Labour and the possessor of innumerable orders and decorations—Sergei Pavlovich Korolyov—was during the last war simply one of the many millions of inmates of Soviet concentration camps and, what is more, was lucky to be one, since the majority of his contemporaries and colleagues were simply liquidated . . .

A Prisoner Decorated

The time came, however, when he was allowed to have his freedom. It has not been possible to establish the exact date on which Korolyov left the special prison, although the year of his release is known—1945, the year the war was won. That was the year in which Korolyov was awarded his first decoration—the Badge of Honour—'for participation in the development and testing of rocket motors for military aircraft'. This was very typical of the Soviet régime: the late L. Ramzin who had developed a new type of steam boiler while he was in prison was also given a decoration when he returned to freedom. And at the height of the terror of 1937 and 1938 there were a number of cases where the award of a decoration to some person was announced without there being anyone to hand it over to, because in the interval between the award being approved and the announcement being made the person concerned had been arrested or shot.

At the time the diplomatic Korolyov, who was usually not averse to receiving all sorts of honours and privileges, greeted the announcement of his first award without the slightest enthusiasm, because his prison years were too fresh in his memory and the contrast in his fortunes too obvious. I learnt from a man who took part in 1945 in the private celebration of

Korolyov's award the sort of comments the designer had to make about it. They were so strongly expressed and so dangerous for him that his friends had to lead him away from the table on the excuse (one which, fortunately, is always readily accepted in Russia) that he had drunk too much and was not feeling well.

It is a curious fact that another person received an award for those same rocket motors of Korolyov's, and, what is more, received a higher decoration. Moreover, the motors themselves were even known in aviation circles at the time by this other man's name: Chalomei. V. N. Chalomei was the designer of aircraft engines at liberty, so to speak, while Korolyov was a designer in prison. After having been a lecturer at the Moscow Institute of Aviation (where I came across him myself as a student) he was appointed to be in charge of the whole operation 'outside', because there had to be a specialist in the business who could maintain contact between the engineers in prison and the outside world. On Korolyov's instructions, Chalomei visited various plants, ordered various components, got hold of the necessary materials and at the same time kept his eye on what Korolyov and his comrades were doing. He supervised their work in the first place as a matter of duty, because it was the job of the outside specialist to see that the 'enemies of the people' in prison didn't get up to any dangerous tricks, and in the second place because he was anything but stupid. Chalomei had access to all the secret documents dealing with rocketry, was thus able to study the detailed reports about German military rockets and realised that the future inventor of a Soviet rocket of the same kind would be in line for the very highest rewards.

Like the hero of Hoffmann's tale *Klein Zaches, gennant Zinnober** Chalomei received both an award

---

* *Little Zack*

41

and fame for work which he had not carried out himself. But he experienced no pangs of conscience on this account, any more than Hoffmann's hero did. After all, Chalomei was a free Soviet citizen who had been entrusted by the Party and Government with the task of managing a group of prisoners who had designed some aircraft engines. Nothing unusual in that, and it stood to reason that, as the man in charge, he should receive the highest award: it was he, after all, who had ensured that the work which had been planned was carried out to time. As for the degree of involvement in the creative side of the work, what self-respecting Soviet leader would bother to go into such technical details? It was the job of a leader to give general instructions and see that they were carried out.

When Korolyov was released from prison and later received his award Chalomei, they say, went out of his way to express his satisfaction. Then, by making use of his not inconsiderable influence in important places he managed to obtain approval for the creation of a new research institute, known as NII 88, specially for the development of rockets. It went without saying that Chalomei himself would be director of the institute, and the chief designer or chief engineer or what have you would be Korolyov.

At this point, however, Chalomei's plans came unstuck. Now that he was in a position to enjoy his freedom Korolyov had no desire to work under the direction of his former warder, Chalomei. Consequently, along with Voskresensky and other members of his group he sent the government a detailed memorandum about the necessity for carrying out the most elaborate testing of all the rocketry which the Soviet army had managed to get their hands on in Germany after the war. Korolyov argued that unless this was done the task of developing Soviet rockets would take longer and would be much more costly because the Soviet scientists would have to invent from scratch what had already been invented. Korolyov also pointed out that most of the best German rocket experts and all their designs were in the hands of the Americans, who would therefore be able to make rapid progress in the field.

Korolyov's arguments were irrefutable. Germany was unquestionably the leading power as far as rocketry was concerned and it made sense to assimilate everything the Germans had achieved so as to advance further. For this reason Stalin gave his approval to Korolyov's project: to organise in the deserted steppe-lands of the lower reaches of the Volga a rocket base and to organise there the launching of German 'flying bombs' as they were then called. A certain number of these 'bombs' had been captured by Soviet troops and transported to an aircraft factory in the little town of Kaliningrad (formerly Podlipki) near Moscow. In addition to that the Soviet army rounded up a group of German rocket engineers and brought them to the Soviet Union, although they were only minor colleagues of Werner von Braun who had been picked up by chance. The only relatively important specialist among them was a certain Yangel. At first these Germans, who could not be considered prisoners of war, lived in a state of comfortable detention in the town of Sukhumi on the Black Sea, in a villa surrounded by an impenetrable fence. They were 'handled' only by agents of the security service whose job it was to find out to what extent each of the Germans could be trusted. For the time being they were not given any work connected with rockets.

Decision and Repercussions

By the beginning of 1946, near the village of Kapustin Yar on the left bank of the Volga a rocket launching

43

site had been prepared and Korolyov moved there immediately. The authorities placed at his disposal the necessary number of people and gave him several fighter aircraft with first-class test pilots from the flying research institute of the Ministry of Aviation.

It was not long before they started to launch V-1 rockets. Before the first rocket was launched one of the pilots, Victor Yuganov, took off in a Yak-3. His task was to chase the rocket and record the height and speed of its flight. If the rocket were to go off its planned course and appear to be going in the direction of a town, Yuganov was to shoot it down.

This particular experiment nearly ended in disaster. Yuganov, who was an excellent test-pilot, quickly got on the rocket's tail and observed its performance from the moment of its launching. But at some point in the middle of its trajectory the rocket suddenly turned off course and Yuganov was afraid it would go towards Astrakhan. He closed up on it, got the rocket into his sights and opened fire from the automatic cannon. But, either because it is always more difficult to hit a rocket than an aircraft or because of the well-known inability of test-pilots to shoot accurately in flight (they are, after all, not fighter pilots), Yuganov discovered to his horror that he had used up all his ammunition, while the damned German contraption was still flying on its way and about to start the descent on to its target. The pilot decided that he must sacrifice his life and ram the rocket with his own aircraft, thus destroying it in the air. He called over the radio: 'Target has changed course; danger of hitting in-habited area; failed to shoot down; request permission to ram'. This message was received by Sergei Korolyov at ground control. Without hesitation he replied: 'Permission not given for ramming; continue observa-tion and report where target falls'.

This dramatic episode revealed an unusual aspect of Korolyov's character—a quality which finally brought him well-deserved success. Unlike the overwhelming majority of Soviet experts, Sergei Korolyov was capable of taking the most difficult decisions and of assuming, without the slightest hesitation, full responsibility for them. There can be no doubt whatsoever that, if the rocket had actually landed on some inhabited place, at the very least Korolyov would have been taken completely off the work he was doing and the Soviet Union would not have launched the first sputnik. We shall see shortly what a monstrous decision Korolyov had to take later, in 1964, and how he found a way to do it.

The rocket episode ended without disaster: the V-1 struck the earth not far from a little railway station and there were no casualties. Yuganov, the pilot, still regards Korolyov as his god. When, later, Korolyov was asked the reason for the decision he took, he offered the following argument: the likelihood that the rocket would land on an inhabited place was negligible, since the total area of inhabited places compared with the area of desert in the region was insignificant. The likelihood of human casualties was even less—they had, after all, been very slight even when the V-1s had fallen on densely populated areas in England. On the other hand the probability of Victor Yuganov's death if he rammed the rocket was a hundred per cent. 'A simple calculation of probabilities,' Korolyov explained.

But the reasons for Korolyov's decision were not so apparent to other people. All sorts of 'top brass'—air force generals and officials from the Ministry of Aviation—were present at his side in ground control. Some of them were offended that Korolyov did not turn to them for advice—that he 'took a hasty decision entirely at his own risk.' Memoranda were flown off to

Moscow, and from Moscow immediately appeared a top-level commission to enquire into the circumstances of the affair. In the end Korolyov was left in charge of the tests, but for a long time while the enquiry was going on he could only guess what his eventual fate would be. Say what you would, he had, after all, only recently been released from prison, and that was in itself a terrible aggravating circumstance which could turn any slight mistake into a crime.

Subsequent rocket launchings were carried out without the warhead: the explosive was removed from the rocket and replaced by a harmless mixture of equal weight. The replacement of the explosive by this mixture was a painstaking and dangerous business and took a long time. Korolyov spent the whole of the summer of 1946 in the steppe.

Chalomei, on the other hand, did not make any journeys to the steppes; he kept his operations to Moscow, where shortly after Korolyov's departure he learnt that the obstinate designer did not wish to work under him. Chalomei drew his own conclusions from this. In August 1946 Korolyov received in Kapustin Yar a decree of the Soviet Government setting forth what the staff of the research institute would consist of. Chalomei, who by that time had been made a professor, was appointed director and at the same time chief designer of the institute. Korolyov was given the position of chief designer of the department of liquid-fuel jet-propelled engines—a department of which the head was to be a man called Glushko.

Korolyov had no opportunity of protesting against this arrangement, and so, back in Moscow at the beginning of 1947 after the completion of the tests, he settled down to the design of a jet-propelled missile of medium range (the sort of weapon which would now be known as a 'surface-to-surface missile') for military use.

46

Meanwhile a rather surprising new member of the staff had appeared at the institute. Although Chalomei was shown officially as the director and chief designer of NII, it was Yangel of all people who took over more and more of the designing work. He had been brought to Moscow along with a group of other German engineers and had been admitted to the 'holy of holies' —the missile institute. In 1950, when Stalin turned the Soviet occupation of Germany into the 'German Democratic Republic', the majority of the German experts went back home. But Yangel stayed, or was left, behind. He continues to this day to live in the Soviet Union.

Since he was a top-level authority on the subject Yangel quickly found out who was in fact the best designer in the institute, and he made every effort to work along with Korolyov. But Chalomei put up a determined opposition to their collaboration, with the result that the two men never worked together in the full sense.

Why Baikonur?

Korolyov carried out the first tests of this small Soviet-made missile at the end of 1947 in the same place—Kapustin Yar. They were successful and all the members of the group that had worked on the new missile were given decorations. They included, of course, Chalomei as well. He, the energetic head of the institute, took immediate advantage of the occasion to press for a government decision to construct a new and larger missile base in Central Asia.

If you were to draw a straight line across the map of Asia from the northern tip of the Aral Sea to the middle of Lake Balkhash it would have to pass through the vast area covered by the missile base—60 miles long and

10 miles across. Situated rather closer to the Aral Sea than to Balkhash, between the Aral Kara-Kum desert and the Hungry Steppe, the missile base had practically no inhabited places in its vicinity. The nearest is the village of Tyuratam, and the nearest town of any significance is Kzyl-Orda, one of the provincial centres of Kazakhstan. It is in fact more than 200 miles in a straight line from Kzyl-Orda to the place chosen for the missile base, but since this remote spot had to be linked in some way with the postal network it was given the code name of 'Kzyl-Orda Estate—50'. If you were to send a letter today addressed 'Kazakh Republic, Kzyl-Orda-50' it would very quickly (only 24 hours from Moscow, for example) turn up in the postal department of the now world-famous space centre of Baikonur.

But why Baikonur? Because all this is going on in the Soviet Union where it is not considered right to tell the truth.

This sad story of the naming of the Soviet space centre will in itself tell an attentive reader a great deal. So long as the Soviet Union was simply launching sputniks—until April 1961—no reference was made anywhere to the place from which they were launched, which was regarded as top secret. But in April 1961 the first man—Yuri Gagarin—was despatched into space and the Soviet leaders found themselves suddenly faced with a very difficult problem. The point was that they wanted to register Gagarin's flight as a world record for height and distance. The Soviet authorities proudly submitted for registration a statement signed by Gagarin and some Soviet 'sport commissars'. But according to the international rules for a record to be registered the place at which the flight started and finished have to be given. After a short period of panic the authorities arrived at the 'cunning' decision to give Baikonur, and not Tyuratam, as the place and thus shift the space centre, as far as the outside world was concerned, a couple of hundred miles from where it really was.

Such acts of deception as this come as a surprise only to people who have not come up against the Soviet mania for secrecy. I shall be describing the whole security system in the Soviet Union in the second half of this book and will limit myself here to mentioning a single fact: On all geographical maps published in the USSR not one Soviet city or town is shown in its correct position with relation to the lines of latitude and longitude. Every one is moved to one side or the other, some more and some less, but they are all displaced. I gather that somebody in the West has already detected this particular geographical phenomenon. We science-writers in Moscow were aware of it many years ago. Apart from that, in the list of matters not to be referred to in the press drawn up by the Soviet censorship (about which I shall have more to say later) it is stated quite clearly that the publication of the geographical coordinates of any town in the USSR is forbidden. There could scarcely be any question of revealing the whereabouts of a space centre!

Almost from the day it was opened the space centre at Tyuratam (as I prefer to call it) was divided into two zones. One 'belonged' to Glushko, Korolyov and Voskresensky and the other to Yangel, although officially, of course, Chalomei was in charge. Glushko, who is now an academician and writes in the Soviet press under the pseudonym of 'Professor G. V. Petrovich', was actually only the man who did the calculations for the rocket engines and spent most of his time in Moscow. The man who worked out the ballistic trajectories of the rockets was, incidentally, M. V. Keldysh, who is now President of the Soviet Academy of Science.

The Cluster

I know very little about the relative achievements of the two groups in the field of missile development. All I know is that, in the course of trying to increase the power and range of the missiles the scientists came up against one insuperable problem: how to construct a jet nozzle of large diameter capable of withstanding the extremely high temperatures of the escaping gases. This problem, in its turn, fell into two parts: to discover the necessary heat-resistant alloys, and ensure the even cooling of the walls of the nozzle during operation. Put into its simplest terms, the position was this: the materials available for making the walls of the rocket engines and the methods known for cooling them did not permit the Soviet engineers to build engines of large diameter, because the materials would not withstand the 3,000 degrees of heat generated by a large engine and the cooling systems were not adequate to reduce the temperature to tolerable levels.

I understand that Korolyov's main contribution at that period was the development of the so-called 'cluster', or group, of small rockets with their nozzles lying side by side, gathered together in a bundle and replacing one large motor. This is no place to go into the relative merits and demerits of a number of small motors compared with one large one. Instead I shall quote the whole of one of the shortest entries in the Soviet space encyclopaedia for 1969, entitled 'Cluster Rocket Engine':

'A rocket engine assembly consisting of several propulsion units (engines designed only for the cluster and lacking certain elements), having common ignition systems, mount, etc. The advantages of a cluster rocket engine over single-chamber engines are greater thrust developed by an assembly of low-thrust units (thrust chambers, turbopump, unit etc.) and shorter length.'

50

As you will have noticed, this laconic and exceptionally obscure note says nothing about the shortcomings of the 'group of engines' system not even about such obvious shortcomings as the difficulty of synchronising the operation of the separate rockets and the considerably greater weight of the whole booster. What is particularly interesting, however, is the absence of any reference to any application of the 'bunch' system in practice. This is a curious omission, because the 'bunch' system is still to this very day the basis of all Soviet rocketry systems used in space flights. Even today, thirteen years after the launching of the first sputnik, the Soviet Union is still experiencing great difficulties in the construction of large boosters and is still making use of the heavy, clumsy and not very reliable bunch system.

It is now known in the West that not only the first sputnik but also the first man (and all the subsequent ones, up to the present) were launched into space on the bunch system of boosters. It is also known that the Americans have long been building giant boosters like those in *Saturn-5**. American experts know that when, in the spring of 1961, the Soviet propaganda machine was having a hey-day following the Gagarin flight and American journalists were groaning about the extent to which America was lagging behind the Soviet Union—some said by five, others by ten years— the main jet motor in the American *Atlas* rocket was still no more than a rosy dream for the Soviet designers. The American experts realise that now. But they did not know it then. But neither then nor later did any sober analysis of the situation appear in the West, and the press continues to proclaim how far the Soviet

* According to information available at the end of 1969, Soviet rocket engines developed about 50 tons of thrust per pressure chamber, while the American motors developed 680 tons.

THE RUSSIAN SPACE BLUFF

Union is 'ahead'—even after the Americans landed on
the Moon.

I remember at the time discussing this strange
situation with a leading Soviet rocket scientist. We
studied extracts from Western newspapers about the
Soviet 'leap into space' and the Americans' 'lag
behind'—and we both laughed our heads off. But then
I asked the scientist seriously and rather sharply:
What's the matter with those people in the West?
Are they all fools? I received a serious and penetrating
reply.

My scientist friend explained to me that there were
three factors working in the Soviet Union's favour:
secrecy, adventurism (made possible by the degree of
secrecy) and the American rocket engineers' need of
money. The launching of a sputnik—the scientist
said—was achieved in the Soviet Union a good deal
sooner than had been expected (and we shall shortly
examine how that happened). The American space
researchers were delighted when this happened because
they had long been ready to carry out such a launching
—unlike the scientists in the Soviet Union. They were
able to use the excuse that the Russians were 'ahead
in space' to extract more money for their work and
carry on with properly planned programmes without
paying much attention to what was going on in the
Soviet Union. Now—said the scientists—we shall
have to make every effort to catch up with them and
involve ourselves in all kinds of risky operations. We
shall finish up badly . . .

Whose Idea?

It is probably impossible today to reconstruct what
Sergei Korolyov was thinking about in 1957 when he
saw a chance of launching an artificial Earth satellite
before the Americans. There is not the slightest doubt

that he knew well how far Russia was lagging behind
America in all technology and in the field of rocketry in
particular. But did he realise then that by launching
the sputnik he was condemning his country—and himself too, of course—to participation in a hopeless race
with a very strong rival? It is a difficult question to
answer, but it is reasonable to suppose that Korolyov
could not resist the temptation to realise the dream
of his whole life at one go, or perhaps he hoped that
his sputnik would attract funds from the military
budget. Then, if the whole of the Soviet missile industry
were working for space research, he could look forward
to engaging in serious competition with America in
the non-military sphere.

But I must repeat that this is no more than a supposi-
tion. The only thing that is certain is that the launching
of the first sputnik suddenly imposed on the Soviet
Union—a relatively backward country—the heavy
burden of being a power in space. It was an excessive
burden which is now no longer possible for the Soviet
Union to put down.

This is how it all happened. By 1957 Korolyov's
rockets, constructed on the bunch system, were, in
various forms, included in the armament of the rocket
forces of the Soviet Army as long-range ground-to-
ground missiles. The range of rockets intended for a
different purpose developed by Chalomei and Yangel
was considerably less. Nevertheless Korolyov was constantly beset for several years by all kinds of intrigues
and attacks on the part of his powerful rival. Chalomei
was far superior to Korolyov in terms of diplomatic
skills. When, following Stalin's death, Korolyov devised
his cluster system to build a rocket engine capable of
carrying a nuclear warhead and was then bestowed
with every kind of award, Chalomei found an original
way of replying to him: he took Khrushchev's son,
Sergei, on to his staff and proceeded to favour him

53

with rapid promotion. In a short time the young man, who was, incidentally, by no means without ability, became Chalomei's deputy, a doctor of science and was even awarded a Lenin Prize. With a deputy so closely related to the country's ruler Chalomei felt very sure of himself and created an impenetrable wall of secrecy around his design department and his part of the space centre. After a certain time even the security-cleared employees of the Tyuratam centre (there were in fact no others) could not penetrate freely Chalomei's 'iron curtain', while at the same time his employees travelled without hindrance into Korolyov's zone on the excuse that the main centre of the whole complex —shops, cinemas, and so forth—was situated there.

Korolyov had no love at all for secrecy, which he found to be only an additional burden in his work. Consequently Chalomei's people knew every detail of what was going on in Korolyov's section, while he knew very little about what they were up to. But both sections were working exclusively on military rockets. The difference was that all the snags, failure and troubles that occurred in Korolyov's outfit became known immediately to the highest authorities, while the blunders made by Chalomei and Yangel were never revealed. What is more Chalomei, now reinforced by his deputy, S. Khrushchev, had close contacts with people in authority and was well favoured by them, while Korolyov was always experiencing unpleasantnesses.

At the beginning of 1957 Korolyov found himself coming across ever more frequent suggestions in the American press that in the course of the International Geophysical Year the United States intended to launch an artificial Earth satellite. The problem of launching such a satellite was being discussed freely in American reviews, which went into all the details of the project, including the cost. There were even hints of the name given to the satellite—*Vanguard*—and there were complaints that the President and Congress were not very well disposed towards the idea of spending millions of dollars on a satellite. We know now that this was absolutely true: the late President Eisenhower had no interest at all in any propaganda effect the launching might have, and no one put such an idea into his head. If the President had known what was going to happen he would probably not have postponed the realisation of Werner von Braun's long-cherished project, and then America would have launched her satellite before the International Geophysical Year began.

But the project was 'frozen', and the campaign which then started up in the American scientific press was aimed at getting it carried out at least within the Geophysical Year, which was due to start in July and in actual fact to last not just a year but a year and a half—to the end of 1958.

Today it is very difficult to guess what would have happened if Eisenhower had given his agreement sooner. Or if the American press had remained silent about the forthcoming launching of a satellite. It is possible that the Soviet Union would not have joined in the space race to this very day, because there would after all, have been no propaganda benefit to derive from it. It is possible that, without having the fear of Soviet competition, the Americans would not have been in such a hurry to land on the Moon and would thus have saved themselves thousands of millions of dollars. It is possible that many political events on this Earth would have turned out quite differently if the Soviet Union had not had the possibility of exercising a form of missile blackmail, sustained to a large extent by the first sputnik.

All that is possible, but there is no point in speculating about it today. But it is worth-while recording one simple fact: *that before the publication in the American press of material about artificial Earth satellites, neither Korolyov nor anybody else in the Soviet Union had even thought about carrying out space research by this means in the near future.*

If this fact can be confirmed beyond any doubt then, obviously, all the myths about Soviet 'priority' in space will be reduced to nothing. And it *can* be confirmed beyond any doubt.

The best confirmation of this most important fact appeared in a Soviet review—Moscow No. 12 for 1969. Once again either the censor slipped up or somebody failed to realise how important a secret had been revealed by the author of an article which appeared in the review entitled *Academician Korolyov*. The author—P. Astashenkov, to whom I have already referred—quoted Korolyov himself on page 167 of the review. In reply to the question about how he arrived at the idea of launching the first sputnik, Korolyov, outspoken and good-natured as ever, explained: 'We followed closely the reports of preparations going on in the United States of America to launch a sputnik called, significantly, *Vanguard*. It seemed to some people at the time that it would be the first satellite in space. So we then reckoned up what we were in a position to do, and we came to the conclusion that we could lift a good 100 kilogrammes (220 lbs) into orbit. We then put the idea to the Central Committee of the Party, where the reaction was: "It's a very tempting idea. But we shall have to think it over . . ." In the summer of 1957 I was summoned to the Central Committee offices. The 'O.K.' had been given. That was how the first sputnik was born. It went into orbit without a permit.'

The most important words here are 'in the summer of 1957'. We must not forget that the sputnik was actually launched on 4 October of the same year.

56

If we were even to assume that the word 'summer' means the month of June (though we shall soon see that there are reasons to believe it meant August), then it appears that four months before the launching of the first sputnik there had been no preparations for such a launching in the Soviet Union, since such preparations simply could not begin in any of the carefully protected designing offices with all their rigid discipline without a specific instruction from the Party.

There was, of course, no question at the time of Korolyov's reply, which I have quoted above, being published: the interview was marked 'Top Secret' and was intended only as an historical record. This is why it contains a number of other revelations. In the first place it admitted that the Americans were ahead in the space race—'We followed closely reports of preparations going in the United States of America to launch a sputnik.' Then there is the fact that the application to the Central Committee of the Party for permission came after the reports in American publications and caught the Party leaders unprepared. ('. . . a tempting idea. But we shall have to think it over . . .') Again, and this is perhaps the most important revelation, there is the word 'tempting', dropped apparently accidentally by Korolyov. This suggests the tactics Korolyov adopted when he approached the Central Committee. It looks as though he dealt very little with the scientific side of the launching, but concentrated rather on the colossal propaganda effect, on the 'temptation' which the launching of the first sputnik represented for the Soviet leaders from the point of view of prestige and bluff.

It was at that time that Khrushchev was most given to boasting that he intended to 'overtake America'. Korolyov was in fact offering him a real chance of doing so. It was that which made Korolyov's proposal so 'tempting'.

On the other hand, Korolyov was taking a considerable risk. The rocket which he was going to use to launch the sputnik had gone through its first tests only in August. This fact was published in the Soviet press at the time and later repeated in all the biographies of Korolyov. He was obviously going to have a desperate race against time, and he placed all his hopes in two circumstances. The first was that Khrushchev would spare nothing in the interests of propaganda—and, in fact, Korolyov immediately had the whole of the NII 88 research institute placed at his entire disposal, as well as a factory in Kaliningrad. The second factor was that Korolyov knew from the American press that it was unlikely that the first launching would take place in America before the end of the year. After all, the Americans were in no hurry.

Nevertheless the risk had to be reduced to a minimum. Korolyov realised that it would be sufficient to launch something into orbit round the Earth before the Americans—any object which could be made to send out a signal and so convince the world of its existence. For this reason he decided from the outset that the sputnik should be as simple as possible and should contain only a sufficiently powerful radio transmitter. The same P. Astashenkov says on this point: 'Sergei Pavlovich proposed that nothing should be done to complicate the construction of the first sputnik, that it should be made as simple as possible. It came to be known as 'P.S.' (standing for "the simplest sputnik")'.

'The Simplest'

Korolyov's biographer does not say, of course, *why* the designer was so anxious to keep the sputnik so simple. But we now know the reason: he was out to save every minute of time and he knew he could construct a simple sputnik quicker than a more complex one.

Strange though it may seem, the rocket caused Korolyov less concern than the sputnik itself. The rocket was, after all, ready and needed only some slight modification involved in the attachment of the new sputnik to the top, second stage in place of the warhead. This also took a certain amount of time, of course, and Korolyov lived day and night at the Kaliningrad factory where the stages of the rocket and the sputnik were being assembled in neighbouring workshops. It is said that in the last few days before the launching Korolyov no longer referred to the blueprints: he simply supervised the attachment of the sputnik to the rocket 'on the spot', as the engineers say; with the aid of his brilliant intuition as an engineer and his experience in the special prison he simply stood there giving instructions about what was to be done and how it was to be done. He had the advantage in this of the services of such a brilliant assistant as L. Voskresensky, who understood Korolyov almost without words, and a group of specially elected technicians and highly skilled workers. Korolyov openly promised them all 'golden rain' the moment the sputnik went into orbit and they worked long hours without sparing themselves.

The 'golden rain' did indeed descend on all the people who helped to prepare the sputnik. Even the women who cleaned the premises in which it was assembled each received three months' pay as a bonus, and the better paid the job the bigger the bonuses. At that time a cleaning woman received rather less than ten roubles a week (the equivalent of four pounds a week at present rates, but less in real purchasing power), while people like Academician Glushko who took a direct part in the work received 350 roubles a week.

59

Even today the manager or chief engineer of a Soviet factory receives fifteen times as much as the average worker and twenty times as much as a cleaning women.

The Soviet press published an extract from the reminiscences of an engineer who had worked on the first sputnik in Korolyov's group. The following passage provides a reasonable picture of Korolyov's frame of mind and the feelings he was experiencing at the period. The engineer recalls:

'I used to like watching Sergei Pavlovich from a distance, so that he was not aware of being observed. He would often come late at night into the workshop where the huge body of the rocket was resting on its stocks. He would dismiss the engineers and designers who accompanied him and sit in silence some distance from the rocket. He would have the most pensive expression on his face, and he would sit there thinking. Then, *as though he had suddenly rid himself of the thoughts in which he had just been absorbed* (my emphasis—L.V.) he would rise briskly to his feet. The expression on his face would change completely. There would follow a torrent of peremptory, clear, precise instructions. The problem was not to miss what he said.'

The fact that Korolyov was so often lost in his thoughts means nothing to readers in the Soviet Union, for whom this passage was intended. The majority of the population of the Soviet Union, deafened by round-the-clock propaganda about 'our brilliant victories in space', knew nothing about Korolyov's past or about how the idea of the first sputnik first came about. There is not a single ordinary person in the Soviet Union who realises that before the first sputnik was launched Sergei Korolyov lived under the threat of his powerful rival, Chalomei, who was green with envy and ready to put paid to Korolyov's career at once if he failed in his enterprise. Soviet citizens do not understand that at that time Korolyov

60

was thinking about another rival as well—the United States of America. The little sphere, less than two feet in diameter, alongside which Korolyov sat, lost in thought, was bound to bring into action all the vast resources of that particular rival. Sergei Korolyov certainly had plenty to reflect on in those decisive days of his life. It was, after all, already too late to retreat.

Actually everything I know about Korolyov suggests he would have opposed any suggestion of retreating. It seems very unlikely that he would have wanted to turn back once he had engaged in the biggest gamble in his life. He wasn't the sort of person to do that. All the same, he knew very well that he was involved in a very risky enterprise, in a game of bluff, that very soon other similar enterprises and more bluffing would be required, and that there was no easy way out of this particular game. Korolyov was better aware of the backwardness of Soviet technology than anyone. After all, rockets were the country's most important industrial product, yet it had not been possible to obtain for them the heat-resistant alloys or the modern plastics, or the miniature electronic systems or a hundred other necessary components.

Korolyov of all people knew that a Soviet design engineer had continually to resort to the strangest devices, to find ways round the problems facing him and substitutes for all sorts of things, whereas the American or Western engineer had simply to order materials and components which were already in existence and well-known. The smallest piece of equipment—a precision valve or a membrane suitable for fitting to a non-standard burner—became a gigantic problem. Such problems had to be resolved every day at the highest level with tremendous loss of time, unbelievable expense and extreme nervous strain.

61

The Unusual Difficulties

I shall now permit myself a brief digression from the central theme of this chapter to illustrate the situation in Soviet industry.

In the course of my imprisonment I spent a certain period in a prison camp situated practically in the centre of Moscow, at No. 46, Shabolovka Street, immediately opposite the old television tower. The camp for 700 prisoners was attached to a small factory manufacturing small engineering components—mainly oil seals—from leather and rubber. The leather workshop in this factory had in fact an *absolute monopoly* in the whole of the Soviet Union in the production of leather oil-seals of every imaginable diameter and shape. If that workshop had happened to be burnt down or to have gone out of production for some reason, it would have been a major disaster, because it would have put one branch of the nation's industry after another out of action. Because leather seals are an essential part of all kinds of machines, presses, lathes, hoists, rail tipping wagons and so forth.

The reason why prisoners had been selected to work at the factory was probably because of their 'reliability'. The availability and capacity for work of prisoners is after all guaranteed by the toughest of all Stalinist organisations—the Ministry of Internal Affairs. The people who organised the factory doubtless had in mind that with such a work force there ought to be no shortage of labour, no absenteeism, no lateness or drunkeness and no disputes about conditions of work. Moreover, when necessary, it would be possible to make the prisoners work on Sundays, as, in fact, often happened.

In actual fact labour discipline was on a high level. On the other hand it was the factory machinery which was strikingly out of date. Presses that were operated by hand, mechanical shears instead of power-driven ones, and vats for soaking the leather which had to be

62

filled by hand—it all looked as if it had been handed down from the previous century. Indeed, in the mechanical workshop, which had the job of maintaining the machinery in working order, there was a *Munchen* lathe still being used which had in fact been made in the nineteenth century—in 1896!

The factory produced twenty thousand different kinds of leather seals, if all the various types and sizes are reckoned up, and it despatched them to thousands of plants throughout the country. But none of them was able simply to send an order for a particular product to the factory. In order to order anything you had first of all to obtain from the State Planning Commission a so-called 'leather allotment', which was a document authorising the factory to use up a certain amount of leather for the needs of a particular customer. Next you had to submit a list of the products required and indicate clearly the quantity of each to be manufactured for a year ahead. Finally you had to agree on the specifications and drawings, which was the most difficult task of all, because it was impossible to produce any complicated seals on the ancient machinery at the factory's disposal. Whenever a customer came along with a very complicated specification he was refused, and it frequently happened that because of a refusal the customer was obliged to introduce changes in the design of his machines—in fact, to adapt the machine to the available seals. There were other cases where the customer tried to make the factory accept his specification by complaining to the highest authorities—the Council of Ministers and the Central Committee of the party—insisting on the supreme importance of his own product. It sometimes happened that on such occasions the Central Committee would instruct the Ministry of Internal Affairs (not the factory, of course, because people at the top think only in terms of ministries) to 'ensure the fulfilment of an important

63

defence contract'. Panic would then reign in the factory, various generals from the security services would appear and the imprisoned engineers and technicians would be made to work night and day, devising some complicated tool to fit to the existing hand-operated press. As a result the output of other kinds of products would drop sharply, and the same Central Committee would receive complaints from other enterprises— also very important and also concerned with 'defence'— to the effect that 'the fulfillment of orders of especial importance to the State is being held up'. This sort of panic situation was repeated time and again, and I don't recall a time when the work went ahead smoothly, normally and without incident although I spent four years in that factory—up to the death of Stalin.

Today No. 46, Shabolovka Street is no longer a prison camp, but the factory remains there. Its work-people are no longer prisoners, and it now belongs to the department of local industry of the Moscow City Council. Nevertheless the periodic outbreaks of panic over particular orders, the bargaining over the manu-facture of complicated items and the complaints to the Central Committee of the Party—all this continues. Even today that factory retains its monopoly over the production of hundreds of items.

That is just one, relatively unimportant example. There are thousands more, even stranger examples. All Soviet experimental institutes, including those dealing with atomic research and rocketry, invariably have their own glass-blowing workshops of the most primitive kind, and a really skilled glass-blower is valued more highly than the most experienced engineer. This is because there is nowhere in the Soviet Union where you can order articles to be made from glass of a particular composition and special shape. Theoretically it *is* possible to do so, because there are 'monopolists' in that business too, but in practice it will take a year or more for the order to be carried out.

President Eisenhower was once careless enough, on a visit to some exhibition, to speak approvingly of a Soviet-made motor-car, the 'Moskvich', as a result of which an American car-dealer immediately ordered 200 Moskviches from Russia as a try-out. The order was treated in Moscow as a matter of 'special importance to the State' and the factory concerned set about manufacturing 200 'supercars', on which every part was specially checked and every car was given a special finish. The snag was, however, that American safety standards demanded that the cars' windscreens should be made from specially strengthened safety glass, and the factory discovered to its surprise that nobody in the Soviet Union knew how to bend it into shape. One of the engineers in the body-building shop of the Moscow car factory had, however, heard of a small experimental glassworks in the city which had apparently experimented with bending safety glass. The engineer went off to spy out the situation, got into the factory on some excuse, spoke with the workpeople and established that the factory had indeed tried at some time to bend safety glass. A request was immediately sent off to the Council of Ministers, which in turn instructed the glassworks—'in the interests of fulfilling an order of special importance to the State'—to turn out 200 shaped windscreens from safety glass in double-quick time. The people at the glassworks realised at once who had been the 'spy' and rang him up to tell him in all seriousness that he was a rogue and a scoundrel and that he had better not show his face in the glassworks again, since all their plans would now be upset, nobody would receive any bonuses and they would all have to spend their time on the new order, which they could not carry out in any case.

I must add that, after a long struggle, they succeeded nevertheless in turning out a certain number of shaped safety windscreens, only to learn later that not a single 'American' Moskvich was to go to America. The reason for this was that an American U-2 plane was shot down over Soviet territory and relations between the two countries became strained. There were some people who said maliciously that there was no place in the world where the unfortunate pilot Gary Powers had so many friends as in that little glassworks in Moscow.

I could go on recounting such incidents indefinitely. Even from my brief experience as an engineer in 1955 and 1956 in a car factory I could produce dozens of examples. I remember, for example, fetching three clutch springs, taken from a British 'Austin' car, from Moscow to the 'Krasnaya Etna' factory in Gorky. Our factory wanted the 'Krasnaya Etna', which had a monopoly in the manufacture of springs in the Soviet Union, to copy the springs exactly for the Moskvich. But nothing came of the idea. The people at the 'Krasnaya Etna' factory studied the Austin springs, sighed, measured them and tested them, and smiled sadly. 'We shall be making springs like that only under Communism', they told me. In Soviet terminology that means 'never'.

Our designers did not succeed in their cherished plan of copying the Austin clutch assembly. They had to settle for something simpler and less satisfactory. The Moskvich works to this very day on the simpler and weaker clutch assembly, and works, of course, badly.

I was never employed in the manufacture of rockets and have no personal experience of the sort of problems that arise there. But I have plenty of friends in that industry who, without going into technical details, assured me that the difficulties which the car industry experiences with the supply of materials and components are simply child's play by comparison with the problems they have to face.

The Great Bluff Begins

To return now to Korolyov—there can be no doubt that, understanding as he did the enormous difficulties ahead, he had in his mind some plan of how to deal with them. In fact it is plain that he had a very clear plan of action, which became apparent from his subsequent actions. In the immediate future the principle on which he operated in his relations with the Government was: give me more, or we shall be beaten. And it worked. After 4 October 1957, when the first sputnik was launched, Korolyov received something of far greater value to him than the 'golden rain'—he had put at his disposal several enterprises out of which he built up something like a nation-wide industrial complex for the manufacture of sputniks.

What Korolyov did not receive, however, was public recognition. Khrushchev took a firm decision that it was not to be and condemned Korolyov and his colleagues to remaining 'ghosts' for ever. These people about whom the Soviet newspapers tried to outdo each other in the use of high-sounding words of praise, were referred to as 'the scientists and engineers who made the sputnik' or 'the creators of the sputnik'. It became the custom to speak of Korolyov simply as the 'Chief Design-Engineer' and of Academician Keldysh as the 'Theoretician of Space Flight'. But today even these titles have disappeared from the propaganda celebrating the routine space launchings. The title 'Theoretician of Space Flight' was the first to disappear from the press when Academician Keldysh was appointed President of the Soviet Academy of Science. Later, when Korolyov died, the title 'Chief Design-Engineer' went

67

out of use. Consequently it is now as though there are no chiefs—everything connected with the Soviet space programme is wrapped in complete anonymity.

The first artificial Earth satellite was launched in the Soviet Union on 4 October 1957. It was a personal triumph for two former inmates of Stalin's prison-camp empire—Korolyov and Voskresensky. But it was also to a much greater degree a triumph for the very régime which had in its day put Korolyov and Voskresensky behind bars, and which continues to this very day to trample on the rights of man.

The great space bluff had begun.

PART TWO

'VOSTOK'—THE EAST

The Political Space Race

There is no need for me to recall the effect which the launching of the first Russian sputnik had in the West. It is sufficient to say that it greatly exceeded even the most optimistic expectations of the Soviet leaders themselves. In fact, the reaction in the West turned out to be much stronger than the impression made inside the Soviet Union itself. This is not difficult to explain.

People in the West were taken completely aback by the way the 'backward Russians' had suddenly overtaken the Americans, whose priority in the development of artificial Earth satellites had never been questioned. But the average Soviet citizen experienced no such feeling of surprise. For many years under Stalin he had had it drummed into him that Soviet science was the most advanced in the world, that all the major inventions in the world had been made by Russians, and so forth. Did you think it was Edison who invented the incandescent lamp? Nothing of the sort—Yablochkov invented it in Russia long before Edison. What's more, the first aeroplane was not built by the Wright brothers but by a Russian military engineer by the name of Mozhaisky. What about radio: who invented that? Marconi, perhaps? Not a bit of it—it was invented by Popov.

At the beginning of the fifties, 'biographical' films were made in the Soviet Union about Mozhaisky and Popov. Mozhaisky's plane was shown actually in flight, and Popov was revealed to have invented radar as well as radio.

It is true that educated people in the Soviet Union jeered at these exaggerated pieces of nationalistic fiction and that wits spoke of 'Russia—homeland of the elephant' when such claims to Russian priority were made. Nevertheless millions of ordinary people believed that Soviet historians had finally revealed the truth about George Stephenson, who was alleged to have constructed the first locomotive, and his predecessor James Watt, who was said to have made the first steam engine. Masses of people eagerly accepted it when they were told that the first locomotive was built by a man from the Urals called Cherepanov, and that the steam engine was invented by an iron-worker from the Altai by the name of Polzunov. I well recall reading an enormously long poem published in a Soviet literary review and dedicated to the discovery of the steam engine by Ivan Polzunov.

After such achievements the Soviet Union's launching of the first artificial Earth satellite was regarded by the greater part of the population, if not as a perfectly logical development, at least as something quite easy to understand and following logically from the successes in scientific research which had preceded it. If 'we' invented the locomotive, the steamship (I forgot to say that the steamship was not invented by Fulton but by Kulibin), the aeroplane, the electric lamp, radio and many other important things, why couldn't 'we' launch a sputnik? It was true that, unlike the inventors of the aeroplane, radio or electric welding (I forgot to mention welding and the arc-lamp as Russian inventions), the names of the men who launched the first sputnik remained unknown, but this did not surprise anybody in the Soviet Union. After all, the names of such great scientists had to be kept secret, otherwise the Americans, who had been left behind in space, would send spies to Russia to steal the plans or murder the principal scientists.

I am sorry if such arguments appear crude. But in fact the names of the people who work on space projects in the Soviet Union are kept strictly secret to this very day. If you were to go to Moscow, stop a hundred people on the street and ask their opinion about the reason why the names of the men responsible for Soviet space research are kept secret, ninety-five of them would give the reasons I have quoted. And if you were to object that the United States is today no longer behind the Soviet Union in space research, that they even reached the Moon sooner than the Russians, and that therefore they are not in much need of Soviet secrets, many of the people you questioned would find it difficult to answer. But most of them would say something like this: If you don't need our secrets then why are you so anxious to make us reveal the names of the Soviet rocket scientists? And they will be very pleased with their 'logical argument'. Such is the power of domestic propaganda in the Soviet Union: it should not be underestimated.

But on this occasion, following the launching of the first sputnik, the fact that the Soviet population had already been 'worked over' by the propaganda machine meant that, although they reacted favourably to the launching, there was not the same extreme reaction as in the press, among Left-wing circles and even in official departments in Western countries. Moreover Soviet citizens realised that the sputnik would do nothing to relieve the disastrous situation they were in with regard to housing, clothes, food, wages, and so forth.

Nevertheless the authorities were delighted. The sputnik had the immediate effect of blotting out the

71

memory of the events in Hungary, although the Soviet Army's brutal suppression of the Hungarian people's revolt had taken place less than a year previously and had had a very serious effect on the Soviet Union's international prestige. In some strange way the sputnik seemed to reconcile both Western statesmen and Western Communist leaders with the Soviet Union. It was, after all, only a year and eight months since the 20th Congress of the Soviet Communist Party at which Khrushchev had made his secret speech about Stalin's crimes. The sputnik, it seemed, was even capable of wiping this stain from the country's image, at all events in the eyes of many foreigners and even Russian emigrants in the West.

Even stranger was the fact that the sputnik was regarded by many people in the world as evidence of the process of 'liberalisation' taking place in the Soviet Union and of a reduction in the Soviet threat to peace. And at the same time, as was to be expected, it produced the required effect among the general staffs of the world powers by demonstrating that the Soviet Union had sufficiently powerful rockets. In short the saying current among the more sceptical of educated people in the Soviet Union—that 'the West knows everything and understands nothing'—was borne out in practice.

Apart from this there was another kind of reaction —plain panic. To judge from cuttings from the American newspapers this was the mood that reigned in Washington. This had the satisfactory effect of ensuring that the American specialists received at last the resources they needed and were able to go ahead with preparations for launching their own satellites.

Watching the Americans

Korolyov knew how important it was for him to keep a close eye on American plans and intentions. That was probably the first time he had ever been really pleased with the Soviet rule of secrecy which permitted him to reveal nothing in advance and at the same time strive to anticipate the talkative Americans. A special office was set up in the NII 88 institute and staffed with people whose job it was to study the American press. One of these people later became a good friend of mine and he told me how they used to present Korolyov every day with a summary of all reports about American space plans and that Korolyov would then indicate which of them should be sent to Khrushchev's personal assistant, Lebedev.

It became clear from the reports that the launching of the first American satellite was planned to take place at the beginning of December 1957. If the Soviet Union was to retain its priority in space a second sputnik ought to be launched into space before that date. And exactly a month after his first success in space, on 3 November, Korolyov launched a second sputnik with the dog Laika on board. The tremendous effect which this launching had was not due so much to Laika (though the whole world wept for the unfortunate dog which had been condemned to death in space) as to the weight of the second sputnik—508·3 kilograms, compared with the 83·6 kilograms of the first one. It seemed as though the Soviet Union had succeeded in the course of a month in constructing a rocket six times as powerful as the first one.

The second rocket was in fact exactly the same as the first one. The only difference was that on the second occasion the whole of its second stage which went into orbit was described as the 'sputnik'. The fact was that the second stage had gone into orbit on the first occasion too, but it was then not regarded as a sputnik. Today it is possible to check this 'innocent trick' from the documents.

In 1969 an *Encyclopaedia of Space Flight* was published in Moscow in several languages. On page 516 of the English edition there is a list of data about the first sputniks. One of the columns in the table is headed 'Number of object units in orbit'. For the first sputnik under this heading there appears the figure 2, indicating that two objects went into orbit—the sputnik itself and the last stage of the rocket. But for the second sputnik there is the figure 1—it was in fact the last stage of the rocket.

Then, on 6 December 1957, something happened which caused Khrushchev unbelievable pleasure but pleased Korolyov himself to a much lesser degree. An American attempt to launch a sputnik (satellite) ended in failure. The American press was full of jeering, self-abasing commentaries—one of the journalistic inventions of the day was the word 'kaputnik' to describe the American sputnik. The Soviet newspapers immediately started to reproduce the more critical commentaries from the American papers, but almost as suddenly they stopped. No particular attention was paid to this fact in the Soviet Union, but I happen to know the reason why Moscow stopped reprinting the Americans' jeers about their own failure. On the morning of December 7, Korolyov phoned Lebedev and requested a meeting with Khrushchev. When he set out for the Kremlin Korolyov was in a furious rage and cursing with all his might, though without addressing his curses at any particular person. The same day he told one of his chief designers that he would advise a certain person to re-read the fable of the Russian poet Krylov of which the moral is: 'Don't laugh at other people's misfortunes'.

Korolyov knew perfectly well that once the Americans had started to launch Earth satellites they would be able to do it on a much larger scale than the Russians could. The manufacture of every new sputnik cost the Soviet Union an enormous amount in physical effort and resources and in terms of money. In the last years of Stalin's life a huge and rather ugly, ornate building topped by a spire was erected on the Lenin Hills in Moscow to house the university. It was an exceptionally costly piece of building. Yet it was said that every rocket of the type used for the first two sputniks cost more to build than the whole 32-storey university. What is more, the Army did not want to hand over their precious rockets for launching sputniks. But there was nothing else to be done which might have a comparable effect from the point of view of propaganda.

For these reasons Korolyov lost interest in the launching of sputniks. He wanted to make the best possible preparations for the next step: the launching of a man into space. He kept on persuading the Party leaders— in effect, Khrushchev—to put more and more factories, design offices and research laboratories at his disposal. And in this respect, by skilfully exploiting his first successes, he succeeded in obtaining a great deal.

For example, in 1958 an old aircraft factory in Moscow was handed over to Korolyov. This factory, situated near the Byelorussian railway station, had long been unable to produce aircraft, because it was shut in on all sides by dwelling houses. But Korolyov turned his 'gift' to a most surprising use: he turned it into a centre for developing ways of maintaining life in outer space. An engineer by the name of Voronin was made head of the centre, and the task which Korolyov set him was quite simple: to have ready, by the time it became possible to launch a manned sputnik into space, everything necessary to keep the man alive. For practically two years on end Voronin's staff did nothing but study American publications on patents and similar matters.

75

The Americans Begin

On 1 February 1958 the Americans launched their first satellite, *Explorer 1*. It was followed six weeks later by *Vanguard 1*. It was articles about this one which had spurred Korolyov to launch his sputnik before the Americans launched theirs. A week later *Explorer 3* went into orbit. Khrushchev began to show signs of alarm. In one of his speeches he dismissed the American satellites as 'oranges', thus underlining the fact that they were very much smaller than the first sputniks launched by the Soviet Union. At this point Korolyov received instructions to put something even more impressive into orbit as quickly as possible. And this he did: on 15 May 1958, the last stage of a rocket carrying a great deal of instrumentation was put into orbit and named as the third sputnik.

Of 40 artificial space bodies launched from the Earth in the first three years of the 'space era' eight were of Soviet origin and 32 of American. Among the American satellites there were many so-called 'long-life' ones, which were intended to continue circling the Earth for 150, 300 and even 1,000 years. There were none of these among the eight Soviet satellites. The first 'long-life' Soviet sputnik (due to remain in orbit for 200 years) was not launched until 1964, long after the beginning of the manned space flights. One would have thought that the relative achievements were clear. Nevertheless the illusion of the Soviet leadership in space continued to be accepted as though nothing had happened. The illusion was maintained by the same tried method: the Russians continued to anticipate each venture announced in advance by the Americans.

In 1958, for example, the Americans announced their intention to launch *Pioneer 4* into a heliocentric orbit. The operation was carried out successfully—*Pioneer* was launched on 3 March 1959. But the Americans did not acquire the leadership as a result, because two

76

months previously, in January 1959, the Soviet *Luna 1* was put into heliocentric orbit. It seemed to make no difference that *Pioneer* transmitted a great deal of interesting telemetric information, while *Luna 1* transmitted practically nothing at all; the fact of being the *first* launching into heliocentric orbit appeared to be much more important.

Meanwhile the reports coming from America were causing Korolyov ever more concern. The National Aeronautics and Space Administration (NASA) was considering various plans for organising the manned flight of a space-craft, and the Americans already had at their disposal rockets sufficiently powerful to take a piloted satellite into orbit. Korolyov had nothing comparable. Once again everything depended on the rocket engine.

The Cluster of Clusters

The main propulsion unit in the rocket which had been used to put the first Soviet sputniks into orbit was the four-chamber 'cluster' known as RD-107. This cluster engine, devised by Korolyov and Isayev in 1954 and put into service in 1957, was very far from being an ideal engine. The RD-107 worked well and reliably, using simple paraffin oxidised by liquid oxygen, but it was unwieldy and did not generate enough power. In its very best version the four engines gathered into one cluster and labelled RD-107 developed (in a vacuum) a thrust of 102 tons. Korolyov needed a thrust of at least 500 tons.

Friends of mine among the rocket engineers used to tell me how copies of all the American rocket engines then known were built in Soviet factories on an experimental basis. If it had proved possible to bring even one of them to the stage at which it could be used in practice it would have been adopted for Soviet space

77

flights without the slightest hesitation, firstly because
it would have been possible to keep the secret for many
years, and secondly because the Soviet Union had at
the time still not assumed any obligations under international patent agreements. It was not a matter of
discovering how the American engines were made,
because Korolyov, Isayev and Glushko had in their
hands drawings of all the American rocket engines,
but of the materials and technical knowledge at their
disposal. The engines built in the Soviet Union to
American plans all burnt out while they were being
tested.

It was at that stage, around the middle of 1959, that
Korolyov came up with another of his 'mad schemes'.
He proposed making a 'cluster of clusters'—combining
together five four-chamber engines to make one giant
engine. This would mean that the first stage of the
rocket would be equipped with 20 propulsion units and
the hope would be that 20 Lilliputs, as in Swift, would
be capable of lifting a giant.

This proposal appeared at first to everybody without
exception to be really wild and impracticable. After all,
even the RD-107—the four-nozzled cluster—necessarily
occupied more space than any single-chamber engine
of the same power. Consequently the diameter of the
first stage of the rocket had also to be larger, and this
in turn increased the launching weight. It was because
of this vicious circle that the cluster system seemed to
have no future. If they were going to have to find room
for a cluster of five smaller clusters the diameter of
the rocket would have to reach gigantic dimensions
and no matter how many engines were added they
would not compensate for the tremendous additional
weight.

But Sergei Korolyov devised a way of getting round
these obvious and, as it appeared, insuperable difficulties. In the first place he did not try to include all

five clusters in the main body of the rocket. The central cluster, consisting of the RD-108 engine with a thrust of 96 tons and of rather smaller diameter than the RD-107, was set in the main trunk of the rocket. And on the outside of the main body of the rocket four cones, each containing an RD-107 cluster, were attached by means of special hoops and fixings. In this way the additional weight was reduced to a minimum and the outside diameter of the central rocket stage remained the same as it had been with the rocket which launched the first sputnik.

But that was not all. The most important innovation consisted in the fact that soon after the launching the four side cones with their RD-107 clusters were rejected, while the central RD-108 cluster still had a reserve of fuel and continued to operate. In other words, at a certain height, when the rocket had already passed through the denser layer of the Earth's atmosphere, it reverted to being the same rocket as had borne the first sputnik aloft. It was this ordinary two-stage rocket which put into orbit a load which was estimated to have weighed five tons or more.

It was, of course, a very complicated, costly and clumsy solution of the problem. But it was a solution none the less; all launchings of Soviet manned space-craft and all the space-shots to Venus and Mars have been carried out with the aid of this monstrous twenty-engined cluster. There is in Russian as in English a saying that 'necessity is the mother of invention', and it seemed on this occasion to have been demonstrated in practice.

A better idea of the ungainliness and shortcomings of the Soviet monster of a rocket can be obtained if it is compared with the American *Titan-2* rocket which was in use at the same period and with the aid of which the *Gemini* series of space-craft were put into orbit. *Titan 2* was a two-stage rocket weighing about 150 tons

79

on the launching pad. Its first stage had two principal engines developing a total thrust of 195 tons. This proved sufficient to put the *Gemini* space-craft, weighing a little more than three and a half tons, into orbit.

Korolyov's 'super-cluster' had a total thrust from the engines of it first stage of 500 tons which put into orbit a load weighing only 40-45% more than the weight of *Gemini*. You simply have to compare the *Titan*'s 195-ton thrust for a three and a half ton useful load with the Soviet rocket's 500-ton thrust lifting a five ton load.

The disadvantages of the Soviet rocket system are immediately apparent. As I have pointed out, the *Titan* weighed about 150 tons on the launching pad. But the launching weight of the *Vostok*, the *Voskhod* and other Soviet space systems still remains a strictly guarded secret, not to be found in any reference book although many other facts about the construction of Soviet rocket systems have been revealed. According to my calculations, Korolyov's monster must have weighed around 400 tons on the ground, and the greater part of this tremendous weight was accounted for by the 20 small-thrust but heavy engines which had to lift themselves into space.

It is extremely important to point out here, I think, that by launching such a monster into space Korolyov, Voskresensky and their closest colleagues showed themselves to be outstanding engineers, capable of bringing off the most daring and unusual solutions of the problems facing them. They were waging a very difficult battle with the country's backward technology, and in that battle of engineers' wits with technological backwardness it was the engineering ability which won the day.

The value of Korolyov's victory as a creative thinker will be even more apparent, however, if we take into account the further unusual difficulties which had to be

80

overcome at that stage. Of these the main difficulty was the space-craft itself.

Coming Down to Earth

Korolyov knew from reports in American publications that the Americans were building the *Mercury* space-craft which it was intended to put down on the sea by means of a parachute. For this reason the *Mercury* craft was being made from light alloys of sufficient strength to withstand such a splash-down. Originally Korolyov wanted to follow the same path. But the first plan of this kind was immediately scrapped by Khrushchev. 'A Soviet space-craft must land on Soviet territory'—such was the demand put forward by the 'autocrat of all Russia'. That meant there could be no question of bringing the craft down on water.

It is not difficult to imagine the reasons which prompted Khrushchev not to allow a Soviet spaceman to descend into international waters. If it had happened, access to the area where the space-craft was to splash down would have been open to everybody. Western experts and the world's press would have rushed to the spot. At the same time it would have been impossible to prevent Korolyov and his close colleagues from going abroad to welcome the spaceman back. Neither would it have been possible without exerting pressure publicly to avoid undesirable contacts between Korolyov and the others and foreigners, and the names of the men who had built the space-craft would have been revealed. Khrushchev saw in all this a threat to what he held most important—the Soviet system of secrecy and, consequently, the whole game of space bluffing. It is significant that to this very day not a single Soviet specialist involved in any way in the construction of rockets has been allowed to travel abroad. To permit anyone to do

81

so would be to create a most dangerous precedent. Khrushchev said 'No'.

I have information obtained from private sources that, before saying no Khrushchev consulted with Chalomei, whose opinion he valued and respected. Chalomei was opposed to the idea, of course, since the space-craft was going to be launched by Korolyov and not by him. He was already green with envy, especially since, under a decree issued by the Government, he and Yangel were under an obligation to help Korolyov with the development of specific components of the system. Moreover Chalomei realised that if the launching was a success it would be his rivals, so to speak, who would move on to the world scene. Of course he wouldn't agree. Chalomei naturally supported his opinion with 'patriotic' arguments, and it is extremely dangerous to oppose such arguments in the Soviet Union. Korolyov preferred not to oppose them.

He set to work to design a space-craft with a capsule which could be brought down on land. He immediately saw that the main problem was the tremendous weight involved in such a construction. A capsule due to be parachuted down to earth had to be far stronger than one brought down on water. This in itself increased the weight, but on top of that was the fact that the speed of touch-down had to be reduced to a minimum, which meant equipping the capsule with a very powerful parachute system. This would increase the weight still further. Once again, a vicious circle. . . .

But Korolyov succeeded, by virtue of his engineering genius, in breaking out of this circle too. He decided that the pilot of the space-craft would have to be catapulted out of his cabin before the capsule reached the ground and would then complete his descent on his own parachute. This enabled the speed at which the empty capsule descended to be much greater and its parachute system to be smaller and lighter.

82

Apart from that Korolyov transferred all the instruments and systems which were not involved in returning the capsule to earth outside the capsule. His idea was for the whole of the burnt-out final stage of the rocket —its second or, if you like, third stage—to go into orbit. The upper part of this stage, next to the capsule, accommodated the instrument compartment and the whole of the apparatus for navigation by the Sun, upon which the return into the Earth's atmosphere depended, the pneumatic controls and a number of aerials. As a result of this transfer, although the rocket had to lift a weight of 4,725 kilograms into orbit, the capsule weighed on the return journey only 2,400 kilograms, and consequently the dimensions of the parachute system could be further reduced. Korolyov did not, however, carry the reduction in the size of the parachutes too far. He wanted to provide the craft with parachutes of such a size as would, in the event of the catapult system failing, make it possible for the pilot to land along with the space-craft and remain alive. On Korolyov's instructions the 'chief design-engineer for the support of life in space'—Voronin—carried out urgent tests involving the descent by parachute of dogs in containers similar in shape to the planned capsule. The dogs were dropped with parachutes of various sizes, and the scientists were able to determine the minimal dimensions of the parachute chamber that make it possible for the pilot to survive landing in the capsule itself. Sergei Korolyov's foresight and concern for the fate of the pilot was rewarded in the most dramatic manner in the Spring of 1965.

A Man in Space

By May 1960 the first 20-engined rocket was ready. In actual fact it had not 20 but 21 main engines, because there was one with an eleven ton thrust serving

83

the upper stage. When one of Korolyov's colleagues, an acquaintance of mine, was inspecting the rocket he drew the Chief Designer's attention to the fact that the number of engines added up altogether to 21. At this, he told me, Korolyov smiled sadly and made a very Russian reply: 'Well, it's a good thing it's not 22 or we'd be bust!'

The rocket put a dummy space-craft into orbit, but the dummy did not return to earth. Something went wrong in the rocket's braking system and the craft remained in orbit. Ground control later succeeded in separating the capsule from the final stage of the rocket but that was all. The dummy remained in orbit as an Earth satellite until October 1965 when it began to be slowed down by the upper layers of the Earth's atmosphere, burnt out and fell into the sea.

Korolyov was very disturbed by what had happened and he immediately put a group of designers to work to develop an independent system aboard the capsule for switching on the retro-rocket system. Future spacemen were thus provided with the possibility, in case of need, of switching on the braking system themselves. Once again, the value of Korolyov's innovation was to be proved four years later.

The second space-craft was launched as soon as the next rocket was ready, on 19 August 1960. It contained two 'cosmonauts'—the little dogs, Belka and Strelka. I was present at the press-conference at the Soviet Academy of Science after their safe return to Earth at which Academician Vasili Parin and the biologist Oleg Gazenko 'introduced' the animals to correspondents. I remember how quietly the two attractive little mongrels stood on the polished table in their elegant jackets while the press cameras flashed and the film cameramen wound away. It is possible, of course, that Belka and Strelka had been given something to quieten them down before the press-conference, but in any

84

case it was apparent how well-trained the four-legged cosmonauts were.

They certainly were given a great deal of attention. The fact was that the people who were due to be despatched into space in exactly the same kind of space-craft-satellites would be going through exceptionally painful experiences. To start with, the two first stages of the rocket, that is to say, all 20 of its rocket motors, were switched on simultaneously at the launching. Consequently the overloading on the earlier phase of the powered section of the trajectory was greater than with rockets of normal design—the American rockets, for example. Apart from that the spacemen were faced at the end of their flight with having to eject themselves from the capsule—not a very agreeable operation, to put it mildly, especially for a spaceman who had just been through a period of extreme physical and nervous strain on a dangerous flight. I myself devoted many years to parachuting as a sport, making altogether 207 jumps (118 of them delayed jumps). But the two jumps which I began by being ejected from an aircraft will remain my most unpleasant memory for the rest of my life. Yet I was not ejected from a space-craft moving at tremendous speed and completely uncontrolled at the moment of ejection, but from a comparatively safe trainer aircraft. And in my case it was not after undergoing a very difficult physical and moral ordeal, but after a good rest.

Thus the use of dogs in the early space-flights was of tremendous importance. A group of doctors engaged in research into the effects of space travel on the human body at the Soviet Academy of Science—which later became the Institute of Space Medicine—and the chief design-engineer for protecting life in space, Voronin, drew up a joint programme of experiments on animals. This provided for research and observation on dogs which had completed five or six flights. After the work had been completed on the dogs it was suggested that an anthropoid ape should be given a space-flight and candidates for the role of 'cosmonaut' were selected at the monkey reserve in Sukhumi. But this programme—the first space programme to be drawn up in the Soviet Union which could be called scientific—was not fated to be put into effect.

As usual the cause of the trouble was in America. It was announced there that sub-orbital manned flights were to take place in the Spring of 1961. This immediately caused a commotion. Orders were given that all research programmes were to be reviewed, everything was to be speeded up and greater efforts to be made. All experimental work not directly connected with manned flights was to be dropped. Every effort was to be made to ensure that a Soviet man was first in space.

Korolyov naturally followed the instructions: he reviewed, speeded up and put the pressure on everywhere. He decided to carry out only two more flights with dogs and then to switch immediately to human beings. No one dared to raise any objections, because the doctors and the trainers of the future spacemen knew very well that Korolyov was not hurrying of his own accord. They also began to speed up their work and as always happens in haste, accidents and casualties began to happen.

Running into Trouble

On 1 December 1960, the launching took place of a Soviet rocket which carried a space-craft with two dogs, Pcholka and Mushka, on board into space. It was a routine launching. But next day disaster struck: the braking system once again went wrong, the capsule entered the heavier layers of the Earth's atmosphere at too sharp an angle and burnt out.

86

It was a very serious blow. But misfortune never strikes once, as they say, and on the day after the disaster Sergei Korolyov was taken off to hospital following the first heart attack in his life. Once he was in the hospital the doctors established that he was also suffering from a serious disorder in the functioning of his kidneys—an illness which often results from detention in Soviet prisons and camps.

Korolyov was warned that for him to continue to work after his release from hospital at the same pace as before would be equivalent to a death sentence. At the same time the doctors told him that they could detect no mortal illness in him and that a long convalescence after his treatment might well restore his health completely.

But to take a long convalescence at that time would have meant only one thing for Korolyov: the failure of the attempt to overtake the Americans in the race to put a man into orbit. The prospect of being second in that race did not in itself cause Korolyov any great concern, because he had always been aware of the impossibility of remaining in front for long. But he realised also how Khrushchev would react to the loss of leadership in space. That highly capricious ruler would stop the release of precious military material to Korolyov and would cut his financial backing, so that Korolyov would be able to do very little in what were perhaps the very few years left to him to live.

I have not made any attempt here to reconstruct Korolyov's thoughts on the basis of his subsequent actions, although those actions were revealing enough. I base my observations here on some comments which Korolyov made and which were later included in his official posthumous biography. An especially bitter remark was his laconic reply to an unnamed film cameraman who asked what the Chief Designer lacked. 'A great deal', said Korolyov, 'time and health.'

87

Korolyov decided to go ahead and risk everything. Three weeks later he was out of hospital and working even more furiously than before. Previously he had been competing with time and with inadequate technology; now he entered into a duel with death itself.

But in the first months of 1961 Fate, which had previously smiled on him, seemed to shower the Soviet rocket-men with misfortunes. In February there were two rockets ready for launching: one of them was erected on the launching pad complete with a space-craft containing a radio-controlled dummy spaceman and a dog. In the course of filling the rocket with fuel, one of the membranes sprang a leak and the whole crew working on the rocket had to be ordered to drop everything and take cover, because for some minutes an explosion appeared inevitable. Fortunately the rocket did not blow up. Once the pressure had been reduced and the fuel neutralised Korolyov took the decision not to delay the launching but to replace the rocket with the second one in the few hours left. He wanted to defeat Fate. But he did not succeed with the second rocket either. The rocket lifted off all right but one of the engine clusters immediately went out of action and the space-craft did not go into orbit.

Neither in the Soviet press nor in Korolyov's biography is there any reference whatsoever to this dramatic launching, but the episode involving the last-minute replacement of the rocket turned up in a novel by Yaroslav Golovanov called *The Men Who Forge the Thunder*, published by the magazine *Yunost*. I presume also that it was this same episode, of which news seeped through to foreign correspondents in Moscow, that provided material for the persistent rumours in the West that some Soviet spacemen had lost their lives before Gagarin's successful flight. I for my part know nothing of any such tragedy.

The First Space Casualty

On the other hand I know all about the death of a man I came to know very well when I practised parachuting—a man who was engaged in testing ejector seats, Peter Dolgov. He lost his life in the course of testing out the recovery (landing) system for the future spacemen.

The trials were so organised as to simulate the conditions of an actual space flight. At the height of about 10,000 metres (32,800 feet) a hermetically sealed spherical capsule was dropped from a heavy military aircraft. Inside it was a parachutist dressed in exactly the same way as the future spaceman. After falling freely for 3,000 metres (9,800 feet) the capsule reached roughly the same vertical speed as it was calculated the cabin of the space-craft would reach on its return to Earth. At a height of 7,000 metres (23,000 feet) the bolts holding the exit hatch were exploded off the capsule automatically—'shot off', as the rocket men used to say. A second later the catapult system came into operation and ejected the parachutist along with his seat. Then a small drag parachute opened, followed by a larger, stabilising one, and at a height of about four kilometres (two and a half miles) the main parachute filled out and at the same time the seat fell away from the parachutist who then landed in the usual way.

Before Dolgov took the place of the future spaceman and tested out the ejector system the capsule was dropped twice with a dummy inside it. On both occasions everything worked normally, but pressure was put on to speed up the trials. It was proposed originally to complete the tests of parachutes by May 1961, but the reports from America made it necessary to complete them sooner, and Voronin, who was in charge of this part of the work, received the order to complete the whole programme by 1 March. Allowing

89

for the delay usual in the Soviet system he reckoned he would be able to carry out a test with a live person in the capsule and have done with it. Perhaps that is why he entrusted the task of carrying out the test to the most experienced of all the parachutists, Peter Dolgov.

Dolgov, a cheery, dashing character, had around 500 test jumps to his credit, including quite a number carried out at speed with the aid of an ejector seat. He had been ejected several times from new types of aircraft to test the efficiency of their escape systems. But on this occasion he was unlucky. What exactly happened to him I do not know. All I know is that when he landed he was dead and his space-suit had burst open. The most likely explanation is that his suit had been caught on something as he was being ejected through the exit hatch.

The fact is that there is a great deal of difference between ejecting a dummy and ejecting a human being in identical conditions. I have good reason to know this, since I have made test jumps myself. For example, the dummy will remain quite motionless in the position in which it is fixed in the seat. A human being won't. Even if he is perfectly trained and takes up the exact attitude required (and this is exceptionally important for ejecting) he will still not invariably fit exactly into the silhouette of the dummy. Moreover, no dummy reproduces precisely the shape of the human being who replaces it. In Soviet practice nobody makes dummies to the measurements of the parachutist who is going to repeat the jump. In the Soviet Union dummies are produced in three anthropological versions: No. 1—small figure; No. 2—medium figure; and No. 3—large figure. I do not know what were the sizes of the two dummies ejected before Dolgov; he at any rate was thin and not very tall. Nevertheless, even if the dummies passed through the hatch easily, Dolgov could still have been caught on the edge of the

90

hatch as he was ejected. It was obviously not sufficient
to test only two dummies, and the result was that a man
lost his life. Korolyov's reaction to Dolgov's death was
to take a number of urgent and clever measures.
Firstly he had the exit hatch made larger. Secondly,
he increased to two seconds the interval between
shooting off the hatch and the operation of the ejector
mechanism. And thirdly, he chose Yuri Gagarin as
the man to make the first space flight.

The First Cosmonaut

All the future cosmonauts who were selected from
air force units and put into special training in 1960 were
men relatively small in height and not heavily built.
This had been recognised as a necessary qualification
from the very beginning. But now Korolyov chose
from among them almost the smallest of all—Gagarin.

It is true that German Titov who, in August 1961,
was the second man to go into space, was of rather
frailer build and even slightly shorter than Gagarin.
But the authorities would not agree to Titov becoming
the first man in space because he did not, in Khrushchev's opinion, fit this important political role on all
counts.

It is interesting, as a matter of fact, to run through the
demands which the first spaceman had to satisfy. The
principal demand sounded like a piece of pure racism:
cosmonaut No. 1 had to be a pure Russian by birth.

Despite the Soviet Government's claim to be
internationalist—that is, to have no nationalist prejudices—every Soviet citizen carries an internal passport in which is noted his nationality—according to
his parentage and not his religion. Children of mixed
marriages have the right, on reaching the age of 16,
to choose—once and for all—to have the nationality
of one or other of their parents. And if, let us say,

91

the son of a Russian father and an Armenian mother chooses to be Russian, then that will be entered in his passport and he will be regarded as a Russian to the end of his days by all official departments. Even if the Armenians suddenly fall into disfavour and start being subjected to some form of persecution by the authorities (as happened in the Soviet Union with the Chechens, the Ingushi, the Kalmyks and the Meskhi, and as still continues with the Crimean Tartars and the Jews) the person who has chosen to be Russian will not suffer in any way. If his passport says he is a Russian, that means he is a Russian, and that is a nationality which in the Soviet Union is always favoured.

But on this occasion, in the selection of the man to make the first flight into space, the Soviet racists went even further. A candidate for this role was required to show that he was not simply a 'Russian by passport' but that he was, so to speak, a '100% Aryan'—that both his parents were Russian and that all his grand-parents were Russian too.

That is why the candidatures of, for example, Popo-vich, who is a Ukrainian, of Nikolayev, who is a Chuvash, and of Bykovsky, who is half Ukranian were immediately rejected. Permission was given for them to be used on subsequent flights, in fact it was urged that they *should* be used—to demonstrate the 'friendship of peoples' in the USSR. But the first man to pave the way into space could be only a thoroughbred Russian.

Among the men who had been through the training there were several candidates who satisfied these demands. It was originally supposed that Cosmonaut No. 1 would be Alexei Leonov, a very skilful and capable man, a brilliant pilot and a professional parachutist. But Leonov was more heavily built, and after the disaster with Dolgov, Korolyov's choice was narrowed. In

92

practice there remained only two—Gagarin and Titov, though another possibility was Vladimir Komarov, who was only slightly larger than the other two.

At this point the second major condition came into effect, which was also by no means of a technical or medical nature. It appears that the future cosmonaut had to come from a family of workers or peasants—to be of real 'proletarian' origins. When the first flight was over Khrushchev planned to organise an international propaganda tour by the cosmonaut (the sort of trip of which Korolyov could not even dream) and wanted to obtain additional effect by stressing the point that, as he would claim, only the Soviet system could provide the son of a worker or a peasant with a ticket to outerspace.

Here Gagarin had the advantage over Titov and, even more so, over Komarov. He had been born in a village of 'impeccable' peasant parents. Although Titov was also born in a village, he was the son of an 'intellectual'—a village teacher, and that was not quite so good. So Titov became Gagarin's understudy for the first flight. In case of a real emergency the son of a village school-teacher could make the flight instead of the son of a farm-labourer. But on this score Komarov was no good at all: he was the son of an intellectual who lived in a town and what is more he was himself an engineer.

That is how the selection of the first cosmonaut took place. I am not sure that in the tense situation reigning at the time, when the list of casualties, including Dolgov, was already known and accidents were coming one after the other, Yuri Gagarin was very pleased with the choice. After all, so far two of the three space-craft, prototypes of the future *Vostok*, had failed to return to the Earth—one had remained in orbit, the other had burnt up in the Earth's atmosphere. On top of that there was the ejection procedure to be dared, in which one test-pilot with the highest qualifications had already lost his life.

If such thoughts passed through Yuri Gagarin's mind, he kept them to himself, and with good reason. In the first place, in Soviet conditions nobody was likely to ask the cosmonaut's opinion: he was simply given the order to make the flight and he had been taught from childhood that to receive his 'country's call' was a great honour and that to refuse to carry it out would be a disgrace which could never be eradicated. In the second place, if a would-be cosmonaut showed a special interest in questions of space-flight safety, the degree of risk he would be exposed to and so forth, he would immediately be suspected of cowardice and would be dropped from the training programme at once. The career in the USSR of such people—those who 'did not succeed' or 'did not withstand the test'—is doomed. That is why, when they were in the presence of their superiors, the men who wanted to be cosmonauts always put on a cheerful air, tried not to be too smart in their remarks and to remember as well as they could all they had been taught in their lessons and in their training. Apart from that, the future 'conquerors of space' knew that as far as the flight was concerned absolutely nothing was going to depend on them. The only difference between them and the dummies or the dogs was that during the flight they would make contact with the Earth by radio and later recount their impressions of space.

The attitude of the Chief Space-Craft Designer—as Sergei Korolyov was called in official communications —towards the would-be cosmonauts was one of kind-hearted protectiveness. In unofficial conversations he called them his 'little eagles', and when they were not around he called them his 'rabbits' as well, not in any way suggesting they were cowards—simply that they

94

served as experimental animals for him and his colleagues. In actual fact no one in the world wanted so much to ensure the safe return of the spacemen or did so much to ensure it as Korolyov did.

At the same time Korolyov, who had himself been working at full stretch and risking his own life recognised the possibility and even the inevitability of risk in space flight, especially in the more adventurous form of space flight into which he had been drawn by force of circumstances. Very typical of his views on this subject is a letter he later wrote to his wife from the space centre and which is quoted in his official biography. 'Our main concern is to take care of the people involved,' Sergei Korolyov wrote. 'May God give us the strength and skill always to achieve this, although it is contrary to natural law. All the same I am an optimist, although all my efforts and skills are actually directed to foreseeing and foretelling the worst which lies in wait for us at every step we take into the unknown.'

It can now be said with certainty that this decisiveness in Korolyov's character was the main reason for his successes—and for his failures. There were more successes than failures, because Korolyov was a prodigiously gifted engineer and was indeed frequently able to foretell dangers. And his first assistant, Voskresensky, was an equally brilliant specialist.

The Last Days

It was already March 1961 and the American threat was growing all the time. Time seemed to be pursuing Korolyov like a fiend. He spent whole days and nights in the workshops where the stages of the rocket and the space-craft were being assembled. Seeing the way the 'boss' was driving himself, the rest of the staff also worked themselves into a frenzy at their jobs. Korolyov moved amongst them with an awesome look on his face and, though he deliberately kept his voice low, he reduced everybody around to a state of absolute terror. A passage from his biography referring to this period clearly reflects the mood that prevailed:

'Preparations for a manned space-flight were in full swing. The designer-engineers lived day and night at the plant. When anything went wrong Sergei Pavlovich went immediately to see what had happened on the spot. On one occasion he discovered that there was a small part missing from the space-craft which was required for training work. He didn't get cross or fly into a temper, but simply indicated to the engineer in charge the figure '9' on the face of his watch and said:

"See that the part is here by 0900 hours tomorrow."

By next morning everything was in place.'

They all understood that if Korolyov was sacrificing himself (and everybody knew about the state of his health) he would be utterly ruthless with anyone who through slackness or failure to make a real effort held up the preparations even by a minute.

As a result of this terrific drive two more rockets and their sputniks were ready by March. A failure in the launching of even one of them would almost certainly have meant that the Americans would be the first to get into outer space. After all, up to that point the balance sheet showed only one successful orbital flight with animals and three failures.

That was why Korolyov now decided to restrict himself to the most simple possible launching, consisting of a single orbit. If such a launching were to succeed twice then he intended to repeat exactly the same operation a third time, but with a man on board. Each of the first four space-craft were intended to be in flight for

96

just 24 hours; before the seventeenth orbit they again took up a position suitable for landing on Soviet territory. The landing on Soviet territory became impossible after the third orbit of the Earth, so that they had to wait for the seventeenth orbit which came 24 hours later.

On the 9th and 25th of March 1961 each of the rockets completed one orbit round the Earth. The dogs and dummy spacemen which they carried landed safely by means of parachutes. The dogs were in fact attached to the dummies and went through exactly the same ejection procedure as the future cosmonaut would have to use. These two flights were identical, right down to the last detail; nothing was changed. Meanwhile assembly work was going ahead on the next, absolutely identical rocket which was to launch the next identical space-craft into orbit round the Earth. But in this one the place of the dummy with a dog attached was to be taken by a man—a spaceman, a cosmonaut.

A False Start?

The Soviet press gave a great deal of publicity to the successful launchings in March. This aroused the interest of the foreign correspondents in Moscow who then realised that the Soviet Union was trying to put a man into orbit before the Americans did and were expecting it to happen any day. The correspondents kept telephoning all the scientists they knew, right up to the then President of the Academy of Science, Academician A. N. Nesmeyanov, a chemist by profession, who had nothing to do with the space flights and could say quite honestly that he knew nothing about the forthcoming launchings. But apparently someone from among the Soviet specialists, either as a joke or on instructions, provided some foreigner with 'information'.

97

The journalist dashed to the telephone, with what turned out to be very unhappy results.

On the morning of 12 April 1961, on my way to my office, I stopped at a Moscow newspaper kiosk to buy the only foreign paper in the English language available to Soviet citizens—the London *Daily Worker* (now known as the *Morning Star*). Right across the front page was a huge headline announcing that the Soviet Union had launched a man into space.

A crowd immediately gathered round me and people asked me to translate the report. With great difficulty I proceeded to recount the substance of the long report by the *Daily Worker*'s correspondent, Dennis Ogden, from Moscow. Ogden said that a space-craft with a man aboard had circled the Earth three times and landed back on Soviet territory, that the pilot of the space-craft was 'the son of a famous Soviet aircraft designer', and that he had returned from space a very sick man and that the best Kremlin doctors were gathered at his bedside.

'All lies!', 'Impossible!'—the people around me shouted. There was no similar report at all in Soviet newspapers that day. I shrugged my shoulders and went off to catch my underground train, preferring not to get involved in a conversation on such a dangerous subject as the comparative speed and accuracy of news reporting in the Soviet Union and countries of the West. But as I reflected on the report I came to the conclusion that it could not be true. The first thing that put me on my guard was the reference to the 'son of a famous Soviet aircraft designer'. This could mean only one person—Vladimir Ilyushin, the son of Sergei Ilyushin, designer of the *Ilyushin* series of aircraft. Vladimir Ilyushin was a young test-pilot and very highly qualified, and he *could* well have been a space-pilot. He was very short in stature, light and at the same time physically strong. But the fact was that I knew Ilyushin personally and had been in his house. As far as I knew he was *not* a cosmonaut. Apart from that, I recalled that Vladimir Ilyushin and the *Daily Worker* correspondent, Dennis Ogden, lived in the same block of flats on the Leningrad road. Ogden might know Ilyushin. He could have telephoned him and checked up on the sensation which had come his way, and would have discovered that Ilyushin was ill and in hospital. He was indeed in hospital: he had driven into a lamp-standard in his car and broken his leg.

It would be extremely interesting to know whether Dennis Ogden (who now lives in Britain) knew Vladimir Ilyushin and whether he phoned him on 11 April 1961. It would be equally interesting to know where he obtained his story about the 'son of a famous aircraft designer' who had made three orbits round the Earth and returned a sick man. But I am afraid Ogden is scarcely likely to be willing to answer such questions. No Western journalist likes to be asked about the sources of his information, and Communist journalists are especially sensitive on this point.

There was something else in the *Daily Worker* report that appeared to be untrue: the number of orbits. I knew from friends who were working with Korolyov that they were planning to carry out an exact repetition of the launchings with dogs in March— that is, one orbit of the Earth and a landing in the region of the old rocket site at Kapustin Yar. Why should the third launching involve three orbits?

When I arrived at my office I showed the newspaper to my colleagues and we all decided with one accord that Dennis Ogden's report was nonsense. But scarcely ten minutes had passed since this conversation when someone burst into the editorial office and shouted: 'Turn the radio on quick! There's been a manned space flight!'

99

And in fact we found that it was being announced over the radio, mixed up with all kinds of triumphal fanfares, that *on that day*, that is, 12 April 1961, at a few minutes past nine o'clock in the morning the space-craft *Vostok* had been launched into space with a cosmonaut, Yuri Gagarin, on board. A short time later there followed an equally triumphal announcement that the cosmonaut had landed safely.

We were really astounded by the coincidence. Somebody commented jokingly on the speed with which the Western press worked—reporting on events in the Soviet Union 24 hours before they actually took place. Someone else recalled the fireman who undertook to extinguish any fire in a trice so long as he was told about it fifteen minutes before it broke out. But we all felt rather perplexed, especially since the *Daily Worker* was a Communist newspaper and was regarded as 'one of ours'. We were also amazed at the fact that the ever-vigilant Soviet censorship had allowed that copy of the *Daily Worker* to go on sale a couple of hours before Yuri Gagarin's flight was announced.

I just couldn't wait to try and find out just what had happened. I started phoning round to all my friends who were working with Korolyov, but none of them was in Moscow.

Later, those friends of mine assured me with one voice that the report which had appeared in the Western press (and not in the *Daily Worker* alone) was false and that it had leaked out through someone who may have known about the preparations for a launching around that date but was not informed about the details. As might have been expected, rumours about the 'pre-Gagarin' flight spread far and wide around the country picking up all kinds of colourful additions as it went. The authorities even had to put out a special statement that the rumours were untrue and that Ilyushin, who was supposed to have carried out a flight in a spacecraft, had in fact been in a car accident and was under treatment in the Chinese resort of Hangchow. I was able myself to confirm that this latter statement was absolutely true.

After having pondered over those events I am today inclined to think that there was no 'pre-Gagarin' manned space-flight, with Ilyushin or anybody else. I have come to this view, not only because I trust my friends among the space experts but for a number of other reasons.

There can be no doubt, for example, that Yuri Gagarin made his flight at precisely the time when it was announced. In other words, Korolyov insisted that the radio announcement should be made immediately after the *Vostok* had gone into orbit and not after it had landed.

It is not difficult to understand why the authorities accepted Korolyov's proposal to announce Gagarin's flight at once. It was because, if they had announced it only after the event, it would have been difficult to prove that the flight had taken place at all. As it was, foreign radio stations were able to receive Gagarin's messages and were thus able to confirm to the whole world that man was indeed speaking from outer space.

If somebody had made the flight before Gagarin that would also have been announced once he was in orbit. Finally, if we suppose no announcement was made for some reason and that the unsuccessful outcome led to the decision to keep quiet about it, then there would certainly have been no announcement about Gagarin before he landed.

We can go even further. In 1961 relations between Khrushchev and Mao Tse-tung were already far from perfect. It is quite impossible to believe that Khrushchev should have decided to 'hide' the injured spaceman in

101

China and thus reveal to the Chinese of all people such an important secret as the failure of the first Soviet space flight. This argument alone, coupled with the certain fact that Vladimir Ilyushin did in fact convalesce at a Chinese resort, fully disproves that part of the story relating to him.

All the trouble with the reports abroad about some unsuccessful space flight was the result of the Soviet system of maintaining extreme secrecy about such matters, which in turn gives rise to rumours and various newspaper *canards*. In this case the blame was put on the unfortunate censors who had allowed the ill-fated issue of the *Daily Worker* to go on sale. According to the rumours which were flying then, there was a thoroughgoing pogrom at the censor's office in the post office, which was responsible for checking the foreign newspapers arriving in Russia. And shortly afterwards the *Daily Worker* correspondent Dennis Ogden left Moscow. The Soviet authorities had begun to treat him rather coldly.

The Aftermath

On 15 April, Gagarin was produced at a press conference in the Scholars' Club on Kropotkin Street in Moscow. It was presided over by the President of the Academy of Science, a chemist by the name of Nesmeyanov. At that time no one knew anything about the man who was soon to succeed him as President —Mstislav Keldysh. Neither he, the 'Theoretician of Space', nor the 'Chief Designer', whose titles were to be found all over the Soviet press, was permitted even to be present at the conference. But immediately behind Gagarin and Academician Nesmeyanov on the platform sat a tall, agreeable-looking man, whose features can be seen clearly in photographs which appeared on

102

16 April 1961 in Soviet newspapers. There was no reference anywhere to this man's name, but we science-writers recognised him at once: he was the chief censor on space matters, Mikhail Galaktionovich Kroshkin.

He first appeared on our horizon at the end of 1957, immediately following the launching of the first sputnik. He emerged in a secretive, typically Soviet manner. The censors working on all newspapers, magazines and radio stations received instructions not to pass any reports dealing with space matters for publication without previously obtaining the approval of 'Comrade Kroshkin'. When they were asked 'And who is Comrade Kroshkin?' the censors replied evasively that 'he has an office on Molodyozhnaya Street at the Soviet Committee for organising the International Geophysical Year'. And that was indeed where he had his office, but the plate on his door did not have 'Kroshkin' on it. Instead it bore the legend 'No Admittance for Unauthorised Persons' which was to be found on the door of any censor's office.

As more and more events took place in the field of space research the volume of Kroshkin's work naturally increased, and in due course he acquired a colleague by the name of Khlupov. Later he acquired more assistants, so that he soon ruled over a whole department, although that department remained without a name. Editors frequently had to send letters there when they wanted to have articles checked, to answer enquiries about authors and sources, and so forth. Such letters had to be addressed: 'Soviet Committee for the International Geophysical Year. For the attention of Comrade Kroshkin.'

The International Geophysical Year eventually came to an end, but Kroshkin's department remained, and a new name had quickly to be found for it. The name which they finally agreed on was: 'The Inter-Departmental Commission for Research into and

103

Exploitation of Outer Space attached to the Soviet Academy of Science'. The 'Commission' transferred itself from Molodyozhnaya Street to the building which housed the research institutes of the Academy at No. 18, Vavilov Street. Henceforward all articles about space matters had to be sent to that address to be subjected to their first, preliminary censorship.

Members of editorial staffs—and not necessarily even the editors-in-chief or the managing editors—had had fairly easy access to Kroshkin. They would telephone him and say: 'Mikhail Galaktionovich (or even just "Misha") I've got some material I want checked urgently; I'll slip round and see you'. And Kroshkin, who was personally a decent and well-meaning character, would usually reply: 'I'm very busy, but I suppose there's nothing for it—all right, come round'. What is more, Kroshkin would often run through the article in your presence and put his signature at the top corner of the first page. This was absolutely sufficient for any censor of Glavlit, the general, political censor's office. In some mysterious way Kroshkin's true signature was known to them all and there was no need even for the rubber stamp so widely used in the Soviet Union.

With the transfer of Kroshkin's Commission to Vavilov Street all this was radically changed. There was no longer any question at all of having articles examined in the presence of members of editorial staffs. Access to the Geophysical Year Committee had been free; but entry to the building of the Academy's institutes could be obtained only on presentation of a pass, and such passes were issued to members of editorial staffs only in exceptional cases. Normally you simply handed over a packet to the guard on the door or if it was especially urgent a secretary would come down from the commission to listen to your tearful pleas about the need for speedy processing and to reply: 'We shall let you know'.

104

Apart from that, articles intended for Kroshkin's examination now had to be submitted in accordance with a mass of formalities. The text had to be provided in two copies, one of which remained for ever in the commission's archives. And it had to be accompanied by a letter in a special form which had to give the authors' real name (if the article appeared under a pseudonym), where he worked and what this job was and the sources of his information. The same procedure is in force today.

And there, on 15 April 1961, was 'our own' Mikhail Kroshkin sitting on the platform at the press-conference. His job was to whisper into Gagarin's ear—and into the President's too—the answers they had to give to the correspondents. They said exactly what he told them to say.

This procedure led at once to absurdities. For example, Kroshkin had instructions not to reveal at the press-conference the fact that Gagarin had landed separately from the space-craft with the aid of a parachute. (You will recall that Korolyov had been obliged to take this unpleasant decision knowing that the American spacemen would not have to leave their capsule.) When one of the correspondents put the straight question: 'Then how exactly *did* you land'? Gagarin, prompted by Kroshkin, proceeded to offer some confused explanations to the effect that the construction of the space-craft permitted the landing to take place in a variety of ways.

Very much later, after the flight of the space-craft *Voskhod-1* in October 1964, the authorities announced proudly that on that flight the spacemen had landed for the first time in their capsule, without making use of their individual parachutes. But the inertia with which the Soviet system of secrecy works is such that even in 1969, when it came to examine the biography of Korolyov written by P. Astashenkov, the

105

censor's office would not allow any direct confirmation of the fact that Gagarin was ejected from the space-craft before it landed. At one point the biographer quotes the explanations given by Korolyov to the future spacemen: 'The cosmonaut can land while still remaining inside the cockpit; but he *can also* (my emphasis—L.V.) leave the space-craft. We have made provision for a system by which the cos-monauts will come to Earth separately from the descending space-craft.' Although this talk of possibi-lities and 'making provision' sounds very imprecise, the sense is fairly clear: Gagarin and the others who came after him were to be ejected from the space-craft. But further on in the biography, when the author describes the end of the first space-flight, his hand is once again stopped by the censor. What he says is 'Yuri and the space-craft landed at 10.55 near the village of Smelovka not far from Saratov'.

Yuri *and* the space-craft! You can make what you like of it.

While I was working on this book I learnt from a newspaper report that the Soviet press agency *Novosti* had sold an American publisher the rights in a book about Soviet space research written by a colleague and close acquaintance of mine, Yevgeni Ryabchikov. I shall be very pleased if at last the censor permits Ryabchikov to say clearly and unambiguously that Gagarin was ejected from the space-craft at a height of 7,000 metres (23,000 feet) and landed by parachute independently of the capsule. I hope Ryabchikov will also say that not one of the subsequent spacemen who made flights in craft of the *Vostok* series landed in their capsules. I would be really happy if Yevgeni Ryabchikov, who is an honest journalist who knows every detail of the Soviet space programme no worse than I, is also allowed to explain *why* such a dangerous

and difficult method of landing was chosen. But I am
not very hopeful that he will.

Khrushchev's Flight and Ulbricht's Wall

Korolyov had good reason to be pleased with himself:
once again he had succeeded in outwitting Fate and
had beaten the Americans by a matter of 23 days.
(Alan Shepard's first flight in a *Mercury* capsule took
place on 5 May 1961.) A great many people throughout
the world, and not just in the Soviet Union, thought
that the Americans were lagging behind and that they
had, by making a colossal effort, managed somehow
or other to launch a man into space soon after the
Russians and even then not into a complete orbit.
Strangely enough, it did not occur to many people
that the American flight had been announced in advance
and that it took place exactly as planned. Actually
such a thought could not occur to the majority of
Soviet citizens because the censorship in the Soviet
Union carefully suppressed all reference to all announce-
ments of forthcoming launchings in America. I know
this from my own experience.

But Korolyov was, of course, well aware of the
whole situation, and gave no signs of pleasure. His
response to those who congratulated him was a curt
nod of the head. And there really was nothing for
him to be especially pleased about. Gagarin, his 'little
eagle', had gone off on a trip round the world accompanied by a whole suite of secret police agents. But
Korolyov wasn't allowed to go abroad even under
such protection. What was left of his life could already
be seen in fairly clear outline: frantically hard work, a
hopeless race with a powerful rival which must inevitably and in the very near future be lost, complete
anonymity and not the slightest possibility of meeting
foreign colleagues even on Soviet territory. As for the

107

money and the decorations he received, without their being revealed in the press—what good were they to him if his health was deteriorating every day?

On 21 June 1961, the second sub-orbital flight took place in America. Virgil Grissom had been due to make the flight a day sooner, but for some technical reason the launching was put off. This was reported in the American papers, and the Soviet press reported immediately that something had gone wrong with the forthcoming launching. A friend of mine who delivered to Korolyov a summary of the foreign press for that day described the Chief Designer's reaction to the news.

'Just imagine,' Korolyov growled, 'that there should be a report in one of our papers that, say, the flight of *Vostok-2* was due to take place today but that because of some technical fault we were putting it off until tomorrow!'

My friend started to laugh involuntarily. But Korolyov glanced fiercely in his direction and stopped him sharply with the words:

'What the hell are you laughing at? You ought to be crying!'

Korolyov did not rush the preparations of the next *Vostok* space-craft. It was expected to make three circuits of the Earth, since the Americans were planning to have their next flight make that number of orbits. But it was not possible for Korolyov to bring a Soviet spaceman down either in the area of the space centre or in the Volga region near Kapustin Yar after the third orbit. For that reason Korolyov wanted to change the inclination of the orbit, and he asked Academician Keldysh to make the necessary calculations for the new trajectory. With the electronic computer equipment available in the Soviet Union in 1961, that was work which would take several months. The Chief Designer took advantage of this to go down to the Black Sea coast so as to be with his

108

wife and daughter and have at least a brief respite from the exhausting scramble of his everyday life.

But in the middle of July, Khrushchev caught up with Korolyov even there. He summoned him to his summer palace on the Black Sea, nominally to inform him that he had been awarded another gold medal. As we know now this award was approved by a secret decree of the Presidium of the Supreme Soviet of 17 July 1961, which was never revealed publicly. But the gold medal was only an excuse. Khrushchev's real object was quite different. He insisted in a friendly but quite unambiguous manner that the next Soviet space flight should take place not later than the first half of August—in a month's time or even less!

Korolyov explained to Khrushchev that there was no need to rush things, that the Americans would certainly not launch anything else with a man on board before the end of the year and had already declared that for the time being they would be putting only monkeys into orbit. Korolyov was also able to tell Khrushchev about the launchings of *Midas* satellites with a life expectation of 100,000 years which the Americans were planning; but these were of purely scientific value and had no propaganda significance, and Khrushchev was not interested.

What exactly Khrushchev was interested in was not at all clear to the Chief Designer. What was clear, however, was that there was some reason because of which he, Korolyov, had to rush up to Moscow and embark on yet another 'drive'.

It started and was successfully completed with the flight of German Titov in *Vostok-2* on 6 August 1961. Once again Korolyov came out of it brilliantly: he carried out the flight according to the same plan as the first launchings with dogs—17 orbits and return to Earth at the point of departure. It was true that two such flights had ended in failure, but the risk had to be taken, there was nothing to be done. What is more, the braking system, which had in the past broken down after being for 24 hours in a vacuum, was the object of constant attention on the part of the designers and engineers. They worked day and night on it, testing it dozens of times and did absolutely everything to ensure that it worked as planned. And it did.

The same could not be said of the cosmonaut himself. Almost immediately after lift-off something started to go wrong with his inner ear and this got worse as time went on. He was a sick man when he returned to Earth. Twenty-four hours after he had landed a group of doctors from Moscow put him into sufficiently good condition to be able to fly to Moscow and be received by Khrushchev, after which he was sent off to a nursing home, Korolyov and all his colleagues were richly rewarded, and a few days later it at last became clear why Khrushchev had been in such a hurry to have the launching.

This time the reason was a quite unexpected one: Khrushchev had needed a really good firework display to draw the attention of world public opinion away from the Berlin Wall, which was constructed on 13 August 1961. And it has to be said that to a certain extent he achieved his ends. People in the West said: 'It is, of course, a bad thing that they should have built such a prison wall across Berlin, but on the other hand they certainly have success with their space flights—fancy keeping a man in space for 24 hours!'

Further 'Achievements'

After that there were four more flights by *Vostok* space-craft, manned by the cosmonauts Nikolayev, Popovich, Tereshkova and Bykovsky. They differed from the flights made by Gagarin and Titov only in

110

the time they lasted and also in that after the third
flight they started to transmit television pictures from
the cockpit of the space craft.   But each one of those
flights was hailed in the Soviet press as a special
achievement, inevitably a 'first' of some kind or
another, which 'left the Americans far behind'.   And
none were more ready to believe this than the Americans
themselves!

For example, Nikolayev and Popovich were launched
into space with an interval of 24 hours between them
were said to have made a 'group' flight.   But it is a
well-known fact that every one of the *Vostok* craft were
launched into exactly the same orbit, and that the
alteration in it which Korolyov had once proposed
had never been carried out.   On the seventeenth
circuit in that orbit the capsule was in the position it
had been in the first circuit, and that happened
24 hours later.   The time taken to pass through the
powered section of the trajectory was also measured
precisely to the fraction of a second.   Consequently
it remained only to choose correctly the moment for
launching the second rocket 24 hours after the first
one for the second capsule to arrive in a position very
close to the first one.   If this proved anything at all it was
no more than the reliability of the rocket cluster-engines
which Korolyov had at his disposal.   After all, neither
Nikolayev nor Popovich were able to manoeuvre their
capsules themselves: manoeuvring in orbit was carried
out for the first time by Soviet spacemen much later
than by the Americans—in 1968.

Following Nikolayev's and Popovich's 'dual' flight
I happened to be one of the people taking part in a
television interview with the two cosmonauts.   Before
the interview began I spent three hours at the Moscow
television centre in the company of the following people:
the two cosmonauts, the head of the science section of
the Central TV Studio, Tamara Chistyakova, several

111

journalists and no less a person that Mikhail Kroshkin. One of the journalists would submit a question; Kroshkin would say: 'That question is not to be put during the programme'. The next question would then be submitted, and Kroshkin would turn it down too. The cosmonauts held their tongues, with Nikolayev wearing the most solemn of expressions and Popovich a meaningful grin on his face. At last they hit on a question harmless enough for Kroshkin to let pass. The question was then written down and Kroshkin turned to the cosmonauts: 'Well, comrades, what are you going to reply?' One of them would start to say something, but again Kroshkin had to step in:

'Andrian Nikolayevich (or Pavel Romanovich, if it was Popovich who spoke)—I don't think you should say that. Better put it this way . . .'

Nobody argued with Kroshkin over anything.

At the very beginning I suggested a question about manoeuvring. Kroshkin rejected it out of hand. Then I asked through which window Nikolayev had been able to see Popovich and through which one Popovich had seen Nikolayev, with relation to the Earth. But even this most innocent of questions was rejected by Kroshkin!

Then Nikolayev himself suddenly put a question to me:

'Comrade journalist,' he said in his unbelievably serious tone, 'you might ask me something like this: "Comrade Nikolayev, what is your view about the future development of space research in the world as a whole?"' It would indeed have been interesting to hear what Nikolayev, well-known even among cosmonauts for his intellectual limitations, would have had to say on this subject, but Kroshkin did not permit me that pleasure. He banned Nikolayev's question without hesitation or appeal.

112

Nikolayev was in general the butt of all kinds of
of jokes, often rather malicious ones, on the part of his
colleagues. Here is one told me by a well-known
test pilot who knew Nikolayev well. It was told
shortly after he had been appointed 'Commander of
the Spaceman Team'.

Nikolayev, as the team's commander, is having his
sight tested. He is seated at a certain distance from the
card on which are printed letters of various sizes and
the optician points to a particular line and asks him to
read it. Nikolayev only mumbles something uncertain in
reply. The optician points to the next line higher,
with larger letters. The result is the same. Higher still.
Again Nikolayev is unable to read a single letter.
Finally the optician points to the top line, containing
only two enormous letters. Again only mumbling from
Nikolayev. The optician is shocked.

'Do you mean to say, Comrade Nikolayev, that you
can't read even *that* line?'

'Listen, I can see the very last line perfectly. The only
thing is I've forgotten what the letters are called!'

First Lady

The last of the *Vostok* flights was also a 'first'—the
first space flight to be made by a woman. The cosmonaut on that flight was Valentina Tereshkova, a woman
certainly deserving of sympathy. It was not long since
she had been a simple working girl in Yaroslavl, where
she had taken up parachuting as a sport and come to
the attention of one of the experts concerned with the
space programme. She was introduced to General
Kamanin who was responsible for the selection of
space crews. She did not distinguish herself particularly
on the training course, but nobody was very concerned
at this, because she was not in any case expected to go
into space. Kamanin had at his disposal a highly

113

trained woman pilot and there was only one flight planned to take place with a woman. (As we know, no more women have been sent into space up till now.) It was simply intended that Tereshkova should train as an understudy, to be present at the launching 'just in case'. Since in the Soviet Union the name of the cosmonaut is kept secret until lift-off, nobody can ever know whether the 'real' cosmonaut went into space or his understudy. There was no question of postponing a launching which had already been approved at all levels simply for such a trifle as a cosmonaut falling sick. After all, he played no real part in the actual flight!

Tereshkova was the understudy, but at the last moment became the first space-woman, because just before the launching the chosen woman pilot became indisposed, as women do, and informed the authorities about it. As she went into orbit Tereshkova reported that the same thing had happened to her, but it was then too late. Some time later Tereshkova announced that she felt very sick and dizzy. The telemetry showed, however, that her pulse was strong enough and that her blood pressure was within normal limits. The governmental commission, on which Korolyov had after the launching only one vote, decided that the flight must go on because Bykovsky was also in orbit at the same time as Tereshkova and the flight was regarded as a 'prolonged group flight'—the first of its kind, of course.

Seventy hours later Tereshkova was brought down out of orbit. When she landed in the Southern Urals she was in the most pitiful condition and the peasant women who gathered round her could only wail: 'Oh you poor thing!' They carried her off and washed her, put her into bed in a little hut and when the spasms of nausea had passed it turned out that she was terribly hungry: she had not had a bite to eat for

114

three days. The peasant women immediately offered
her the only food they had—bread and onions. While
she was having this frugal meal a helicopter landed
near the village and took the unusual 'guest from the
sky' aboard.

When later she came to speak in public about her
flight, Tereshkova made good use of this episode.
As she described this episode, the peasant women
welcomed her with open arms and asked her what
she would like to eat. And all she wanted was simple
Russian food—black bread and onions. Stories like
that have an effect on a certain section of the Soviet
population.

Valeri Bykovsky, who had taken off two days before
Tereshkova and landed at practically the same time as
she did, was also, of course, a 'first'. He spent longer in
space than all the others. But it has to be said that, as a
cosmonaut, Bykovsky was the complete reverse of
Tereshkova. He remained in first class physical
condition throughout the 119 hours of his flight.

That is what happened on the last flights of the
Vostok space-craft. The Russians were now in a position
to repeat them as often as they pleased. But the
Americans announced that their *Mercury* programme
was finished. So the *Vostok* disappeared at once from
the scene.

What Next?

There remain a few other curious details connected
with this stage of the Soviet space flights to which I
should draw attention.

From the very beginning, from the time of Gagarin's
flight, the Soviet authorities took great care to ensure
that the Americans did not 'get out in front' on some
score or another—in the number of flights, the number
of orbits or the number of astronauts. Korolyov had to

115

make sure that the Russians always retained the lead in this sense. Consequently, when Malcolm Carpenter made his flight into space on 24 May 1962, and the Americans came level with the Russians in the number of launchings into orbit there was considerable concern at the top levels. Concern became alarm when it became apparent that the next *Mercury* flight piloted by Walter Schirra was planned to take place in September of the same year. I was told by people close to Korolyov that it was this fact that made it absolutely essential for the Russians to launch not one but two *Vostoks* at once in August, a whole month earlier, so as to hold on to the leadership.

In fact Nikolayev and Popovich were launched into space in August 1962, while Schirra's launching did not take place till 3 October.

Later, on 15 May 1963, Gordon Cooper again brought the score even. What is more, the Americans then announced quite cheerfully that the *Mercury* programme was complete. It was logical to assume that the Americans were concentrating their attention on a new series of flights, especially since a plan had already been revealed in general terms for the launching of two-seater space-craft, for the pilot to leave the craft in outer space, and for manoeuvring and docking while in orbit. It would also have been logical for the Russians to direct all their resources to carrying out something of the same kind—and above all to develop a sufficiently powerful space vehicle. But no— Khrushchev and his circle remained in the grips of the 'sporting', or rather the propaganda aspect of the space race. Once again Korolyov was ordered to 'get out in front' and to do so as strikingly as possible. This is the explanation of the final flights of the *Vostok* craft with Bykovsky and Tereshkova aboard.

All six flights of the Soviet astronauts in the *Vostok* craft were accompanied by loud bursts of propaganda.

116

Khrushchev declared that 'Socialism is the best launching site for flights to outer space'. But the people working with Korolyov were simply appalled, because they were better acquainted with what was being said in American scientific publications and realised that from the very beginning of the new programme, with its two astronauts, manoeuvring in space, docking and so forth, America would at once shoot far ahead. Whereas the Russians could not yet think of carrying out the launching of a·multi-seater space-craft, even less of performing manoeuvring and docking operations. Korolyov's colleagues also knew that there would be no delay on the part of the Soviet authorities in finding people to be held responsible for the lag in Soviet space research. In the Soviet Union the authorities are very quick to fix on those who are 'to blame' and to deal with them 'without reference to their earlier services' as the customary formula in my country says.

There was something else that Korolyov, Voskresensky and their assistants knew. The Americans' space programmes were clearly aimed at the Moon, and they had their own internal logic. The idea was first of all to learn to fly around the Earth, then to carry out manoeuvres in space and rendezvous in space, and then to leave the spaceship while it was in orbit around the Earth. This experience could then be applied to orbiting around the Moon with the idea of finally carrying out a Moon landing.

But the Soviet space flights which Korolyov had started with such a scramble in 1957, when he launched the first sputnik, were by this time aimed at nothing at all. The Moon was now out of the question, and it was clear that the Americans would reach it much sooner. Mars was even further beyond the Russians' scope. But a very tempting and, most important, realisable idea was that of putting space stations into orbit and changing the crews manning them from time

117

to time. There would, or course, be similar stations put up by the Americans, but the plan would at least provide the Russians with valuable experience, and the appearance of keeping up in space if the Moon were left out of consideration for the time being.

Voskresensky was especially disturbed by all these problems. He could see that the situation was becoming ever more threatening and disastrous and that the myth of Russia being the 'best launching site' was liable to be exploded any moment, and he believed that if reasonable steps were taken it would be possible for the Russian scientists to bring the situation under control, to end the senseless and doomed space race and to follow their own line of research, even if it were a more modest one. But Voskresensky also saw that Korolyov would not put such proposals to Khrushchev and he himself did not wish to go over the head of his own leader and friend.

The reasons why Korolyov did not go to Khrushchev with some such proposals were fairly clear. In the first place, he realised that the semi-illiterate petty tyrant would immediately say: 'What are you trying to say? —You started it all, you persuaded us that we'd beat the Americans to it and now you want to back out of it all?' Khrushchev was a skilful enough demagogue and would find no difficulty in concocting some formula to hurl at Korolyov—that, for example, he had 'deceived the Party'. That is a very frightening formula in the Soviet Union.

In the second place, Korolyov knew that Khrushchev would certainly not allot substantial resources for the construction of orbital space stations. In his eyes such an objective would have appeared only boring; there was nothing about it to impress the world as he had done with the first sputnik or Gagarin's flight. It would not constitute a 'firework display'. And Korolyov could certainly not work in conditions where his

118

financial resources were limited. He knew why it had
been possible, despite all the difficulties and setbacks,
for him to launch sputniks and men into space: it
was because the resources at his disposal had been
unlimited. Many of the parts which had been made
singly by hand for the sputniks and space craft had
cost far more than if they had been made from pure
gold, but nobody had raised any objections to that.
But if his resources were reduced it would be impossible
to get anything done.

And there was a third reason: Chalomei. If Korolyov
were to approach Khrushchev with such a proposal
the dictator would inevitably hand the reins of power
over to Chalomei and give him the job of organising
the flight to the Moon. The result would of course be a
terrible failure, but what of that? The point was that
it would not be Chalomei's failure but the country's.
And Korolyov had devoted his whole life to working
for his country, which he loved more than Khrushchev
and Chalomei put together.

There were other reasons why Korolyov marked
time and did not go to Khrushchev. As I have described at the beginning of this book, Korolyov eventually
made his report, and a quite frank one at that, not to
Khruschev but to Brezhnev and Kosygin after Khrushchev had been removed. But even before he did so
Korolyov was to go through some experiences of which
at the time, at the end of the summer of 1963, he had
not the slightest idea.

PART THREE

'VOSKHOD'—THE RISING OF THE SUN

Russian Space Technology

It was utterly contrary to Sergei Korolyov's nature to give himself over to a state of passive despair. All his life, whenever he had come up against an obstacle, Korolyov had attacked it head on.

The obstacle which now stood in Korolyov's way appeared to be absolutely insuperable. In the very near future—he did not know exactly when—American multi-seater piloted space-craft were going to shoot up into the sky and before anyone knew what was happening they would carry out 'Kennedy's command' and land on the Moon. But the mere fact of knowing the inevitability of such a development did not weaken the Chief Designer's will or undermine his energy. Since there was no longer any point in launching any more *Vostok* space-craft and since it had not been possible to make a more powerful vehicle, Korolyov proceeded, with his customary wisdom, to 'get his sledge ready in the summer', as the Russians say. He set himself the task of constructing the lightest and most easily launchable space-craft with three seats.

Sooner or later—Korolyov argued—there would be a need for such a craft. The rocket engineers were working without respite on the new vehicle, and Korolyov wanted to make their job easier by making

120

the 'tip' of their future rocket lighter and more manageable. All that would take time, but once the rocket was ready and if the Americans began to put the pressure on, then there would be another rush to get everything finished and there would be no time to finish the space-craft off properly.

Korolyov made L. A. Voskresensky responsible for drawing up the design for building the *Soyuz* space-craft.

As we now know, the *Soyuz* space-craft was first launched into space in April 1967, a year and four months after the death of the great designer. It was only then that the rocket was delivered. And even the first *Soyuz* was launched in its simplest and lightest version, with one astronaut aboard, and it had a fatal-accident on its return. The next *Soyuz*—and the first successful one—was launched only at the end of October 1968. But this extremely interesting space-craft was actually created by Korolyov and Voskresensky in 1963. There can be no doubt at all about this, although it is still unknown to any Soviet citizen and there are very few people in the West who know it.

What is interesting about the *Soyuz* is that it was a logical and, I would say, an economical development of the *Vostok*. Both elements of the *Vostok*—the spherical capsule and the cylindrical last stage of the rocket—are present in the *Soyuz*. But the leading section of the last stage is actually an additional cockpit. It is this cockpit which plays the part of a landing capsule or, in Soviet terminology, a 'descent apparatus'. The whole structure is only slightly larger than the *Vostok* and does not differ substantially from it in weight.

Soviet sources of information laid great stress on the great size of the *Soyuz* space-craft, but were careful not to give any figures on the subject, neither of their dimensions nor of their weight. The point of this was to avoid the disillusionment which comparison with the *Vostok* would have caused. But, wishing to

121

hint at the 'vast dimensions' of the space-craft, the Soviet press reported after the launching that the total volume of the *Soyuz* was nine cubic metres (319 cubic feet). A simple calculation reveals that the total volume of the *Vostok* was in the region of eight cubic metres (283 cubic feet).

The descent apparatus on the *Vostok* craft was a sphere 2·3 metres (7·5 feet) in diameter, with a volume of 6·36 cubic metres (225 cubic feet). Of that the leading section of the last stage of the rocket vehicle —the instrument section—occupied at least 1·5 cubic metres (53 cubic feet). The instrument section of the *Soyuz* is included in the total 9 cubic metres (319 cubic feet).

Korolyov and Voskresensky turned their efforts to building a three-seater space-craft of almost the same dimensions as the single-seater one. It is quite clear why they tried to achieve this: it was because a 'super-light' and 'super-small' craft of that kind could be put into space by a rocket only slightly more powerful than the 21-engined 'monster' which had lifted the *Vostok*. In all fairness it must be said that it was due to the genius of Korolyov and the outstanding ability of Voskresensky—and not to Chalomei, Yangel and the other designers of 'super-powerful' rockets—that the Soviet Union was able from 1968 to start launching into Earth orbit three-seater space-craft capable of manoeuvring and docking in space. This appears somewhat paradoxical when we realise that Voskresensky died at the beginning of 1965 and Korolyov in January 1966.

In developing the *'Soyuz'* craft Korolyov and Voskresensky had of course, at the back of their minds the thought that they would be able to push Soviet astronautics in the direction of building orbital space stations. If that had happened, the Soviet space experts would at least have had a clear objective and each

122

successive launching would have been a step further towards that objective, as was the case with the NASA launchings in America. But so far the only objective had been to try on each occasion to do something that would create the impression of Soviet leadership in space and to carry another stage further an exhausting and undignified game in which they had not the slightest hope of success.

The hopes which Korolyov and Voskresensky cherished in connection with the *Soyuz* were not fated to be realised during their lifetime. Something rather different happened.

Three Men in a Space-craft

There are occasions when, even if you are expecting it, a piece of news has the effect of a bomb exploding. That was the effect created by the American reports at the end of 1963 that it was proposed immediately to start two series of launchings at once—the *Gemini* and the *Apollo* programmes. In the spring of 1964 two unmanned launchings were due to take place—*Gemini-1* with the aid of the *Titan* rocket, and *Apollo-1* on the *Saturn* rocket. The first manned *Gemini* flight and the first space-walk by one of the astronauts was planned to take place at the end of 1964 or early in 1965.

It should not be thought, of course, that this announcement had any effect on the Soviet *public*. The fact was that the population of the Soviet Union knew nothing whatsoever about it. It was in the relatively narrow circles of the rocket experts that the alarm spread. It had in fact long been realised in those circles that such a moment as this must come, when even a man like Korolyov would have nothing at his disposal to match the American launchings. It was simply that the majority of the experts had not believed that the moment would arrive so soon. Yet, as it turned out in

123

the course of subsequent events, Korolyov's abilities were under-estimated even by his closest colleagues.

When news of the forthcoming American launchings reached Khrushchev, Korolyov was summoned to his presence and ordered to report on the situation. Korolyov himself had not been asking for an audience, as we have seen; but now the occasion was offered, Voskresensky insisted that it was essential to open the ruler's eyes and persuade him that all future manned flights should be directed towards the construction of orbital space research stations.

I do not know whether Korolyov succeeded in telling Khrushchev something to this effect. But I do know what he had to listen to from Khrushchev, because a strange report, which was at first not taken very seriously, spread quickly among Korolyov's colleagues and then leaked to people outside. Khrushchev asked whether Korolyov was aware that the Americans were planning to launch two men into space in a single space capsule. (This aspect of the project was the only one that interested the Soviet leader.) When Korolyov answered in the affirmative Khrushchev simply gave him his instructions: 'All right then—by the next Revolution anniversary [7 November 1964] we must launch not two but three people into space at once.'

It was said that Korolyov explained to Khrushchev at length and with great patience why such a feat was impossible. He put all his cards on the table, explaining that the space-craft could well be ready by the appointed date, but that there was nothing capable of lifting it into space.

The Soviet leader was not interested, however, in such boring technical details. He hinted to the Chief Designer that, if he did not carry out the 'task set by the Party and the Government' (and Khrushchev, as First Secretary of the Communist Party and Prime

Minister, was both 'party' and 'government'), then they would have to find somebody else who would be ready to do the job. Once again the figure of Chalomei was dangled in front of Korolyov!

Without making any promises beyond saying that he would think it over, and having been given a very limited time for his reflections, Korolyov returned to Kaliningrad. Stories about his return long circulated in Russia. For reasons easy to understand Sergei Korolyov was not an especially well-balanced person: there had been references to his 'difficult character' even in the Soviet press. He was liable to give way to fits of rage in the course of which it was better not to get in his way. But they say that Korolyov had never been seen in such a state as he was that day, neither before nor after. The word went round the institute in a flash that 'S.P.' (as he was known by his colleagues) had been beside himself when he returned. People tucked themselves away in their rooms, silence reigned over the drawing boards and everybody appeared intent on his work.

Korolyov did not, however, devour even those unfortunate folk who happened through ignorance of the affair to run into him that day. He simply went straight to his office with a stern, glum expression on his face, growling to his secretary as he went: 'Get all the heads of departments together'. That meant summoning a conference of all the design-engineers in charge of developing components for the rockets and space-craft.

Without making the slightest reference to his conversation with Khrushchev, Korolyov announced tersely in quite workaday tones that 'we have the task' of launching a three-seater space-craft into space not later than 7 November 1964. It was that date, the anniversary of the 1917 Revolution, which in fact told those present who had set them the task and even

125

in a certain sense what Korolyov thought about it. When he had finished the Chief Designer asked whether anyone had any suggestions to make. People looked enquiringly at each other and shrugged their shoulders, as people do when somebody tells a very improper joke in public. Naturally, nobody had any suggestions to make. At this Korolyov seemed suddenly to droop, dismissed the gathering with a tired gesture of his hand and said that if anyone had any suggestions, however wild they might seem, he was ready to listen to them at any hour of the day or night. With that he went home.

The next day another similar meeting was summoned at which Korolyov said, looking firmly down at the floor: 'There is a suggestion. It is to try and squeeze three seats into the *Vostok*, at the same time reducing the weight of the sphere by every means possible.'

After a second's confusion everybody started making a row and waving their arms about. Nonsense! Impossible! You can only just get one seat in there now!

Korolyov let them shout themselves out, then said sharply: 'We're going to try'. And the meeting was over.

They tried, but nothing came of it. Even after they had cleared out of the 'sphere' absolutely all the scientific equipment and reduced to a minimum the supplies for maintaining life on board, it was still impossible to find room in the *Vostok* for three astronauts of even the very smallest dimensions.

For a certain period they were unable to extract themselves from this dead-end. Korolyov made no reports to Khrushchev on the subject, still hoping to gain time. But the winter of 1964 was already coming to an end. Unable to stand the nervous strain, Voskresensky collapsed and was put into hospital.

It is interesting to see how Korolyov's official Soviet biographer describes the difficult mood in which the Chief Designer was at that time. There is, of course, not the slightest reference in the biography to the existence of any problems or to the snags which work on the *Voskhod* had come up against. The following passage, quoted from the magazine *Moscow* (No. 12 for 1969, p. 178), sounds consequently all the stranger: 'In the course of his work on the *Voskhod* Sergei Pavlovich displayed especially forcibly his unusually demanding nature and his utter lack of sympathy for any defects or human weaknesses. He had no time for them, either in himself or in others'.

To say of anyone that he had no sympathy for human weaknesses is to pay him a very doubtful compliment indeed. But, with the knowledge that we now have, we can, I think, easily defend Korolyov from his own biographer. In the situation which had come about at the time I doubt whether the nerves of the most angelic of angels would have held out. After all, Korolyov knew perfectly well that he was being forced to embark on a wild adventure and one, moreover, which was known to be pointless. It had been laid down that before two Americans could be launched into space at the same time three Soviet citizens had to do the same—that was all there was to it!

The Voskhod Adventure

The problem of working out how to send three people into space was solved in the following way: the three men were squeezed into the *Vostok* module *without their space-suits*, so that they had to rely entirely on the hermetic sealing of the craft. It is said that it was the leading designer of descent apparatus Konstantin Feoktistov, who suggested this madly, daring and risky solution. And when Korolyov asked: 'But who on earth is going to fly without his space suit?', Feoktistov replied: 'I will for one'. That was how the leading designer, a man of far from perfect health who

127

had been wounded in his youth, suddenly became an astronaut.

But even with this modification—with the astronauts in their underwear—it was still not possible to find room for three of them in the long-suffering *Vostok*, which was renamed the *Voskhod* for the sake of appearances.

The designers then began trying out the wildest ideas. Feoktistov quickly reached agreement with Korolyov and all the principal departments on the composition of the crew—a young doctor of very small stature by the name of Yegorov, the best of the pilots among the astronauts, Komarov, and himself—and all three of them went off for a sitting with a sculptor! The artist then made seats exactly to fit the shape of each of them. Then, under Korolyov's 'ruthless' direction, three dummies were rapidly constructed to the shape of the seats. But it was still found impossible to fit them into the capsule.

Then somebody had another idea. It was suggested that the seats should not be set side by side but in a less obvious fashion, perhaps one in front and two behind, so as to form a sort of triangle. It was thought that such a triangle would fit in better.

At first even this did not work out, but later, after the leading seat had been brought so close to the ones behind that one of the astronauts was practically sitting on the others' knees, it was found that the capsule would hold all of them. Doctor Yegorov, being the smallest of them, was put right up front, and this made it possible to raise his seat in relation to the other two. In this way the doctor was in the flight commander's seat, while the commander himself was sitting somewhere behind and underneath him, but this was of no real importance, since none of the crew was in any case going to perform any operations in the course of the flight!

A very sick joke went the rounds of the institute at the time, to the effect that the staff were working all-out

128

on the construction of a perfect space-grave for three people. There was a certain truth behind this grim humour in that, with such an arrangement in the capsule, to have ejected the three men would have meant their almost certain death. But whoever coined the joke was not apparently aware of something else: that Korolyov had decided not to eject the astronauts but to bring the whole capsule down on parachutes.

It was in fact unthinkable to take any other decision. All the previous six astronauts had been ejected from the *Vostok* craft at a height of 7,000 metres (23,000 feet). It was not possible to reduce the height at which the ejection took place because that would have exposed the astronauts to the risk of almost certain death. But to be ejected at a height of 23,000 feet a man must be wearing a space-suit. But space-suits were out of the question. It is true that, with proper training, a man can survive at a height of 23,000 feet without a protective suit if he is equipped with an oxygen apparatus. But the astronauts were packed in the capsule like sardines in a tin, and they could not be provided with such an apparatus because there was nowhere to put the oxygen cylinders.

As I have already recounted, Korolyov and Voronin, the chief design-engineer for maintaining life in space, had already tested the possibility of bringing the *Vostok* down by parachute. But those tests had taken place only to discover the 'critical impact', that is the maximum force of the blow which a living creature could survive. It was of course impossible to submit the astronauts to such a blow, so they had to increase the size of the two parachutes contained in the capsule and go through the whole test process again. At this point the doctors declared that an impact which a dog might be capable of surviving might nevertheless prove fatal for a human being. They said they could give a guarantee that a man would survive the shock

129

only after experiments had been made with large monkeys, which are more sensitive even than human beings.

Three monkeys who were dropped in a capsule with specially strengthened parachutes were found to be dead in their seats on reaching the ground.

There followed the only occasion in the whole of Sergei Korolyov's career when his customary resolution and capacity to take risks deserted him. He faltered, hesitating whether to go on with a risky enterprise which was becoming more senseless every day or to refuse to go on with it and prepare to take the most unpleasant consequences.

That this was his state of mind at that time is confirmed in Korolyov's official biography which, though written with the aims of concealing some facts and embellishing others, still follows the chronology of his life. Astashenkov's biography is rather like a plaster façade badly applied to a brick wall. It follows the general shape of the wall, and if you poke into it you occasionally expose some bricks, or facts, concealed beneath an unreliable surface of lies.

We read in it, for example: 'There were difficulties and failures. In the course of one test, on account of a fault in the landing system, the space-craft did not make an entirely "soft" landing on the Earth'.

'After this failure Sergei Pavlovich asked Konstatin Feoktistov: "Aren't you afraid to fly in it? The sphere crashed".'

The biographer goes on to say that Feoktistov replied that he was not afraid. This is not so important (though Feoktistov probably did reply in that way) as the question put by the 'tough' Korolyov to the only one of the astronauts who was fully informed about all the details of the construction of the capsule. 'Aren't you afraid? The sphere crashed.' Never before or

130

afterwards did Korolyov put such a diffident question to one of his subordinates.

Oddly enough, the passage from the biography which I have quoted is the only official Soviet source to describe the *Voskhod* space-craft as a 'sphere'. The censorship, including Kroshkin himself, clearly let the word 'sphere' slip through by mistake. The ban on the publication of any drawings whatsoever of the *Voskhod* space-craft is still in force to this day. The *Vostok* space-craft and the later *Soyuz* craft are put on display for inspection even at international exhibitions, but nowhere has there ever been published even the smallest photograph of the *Voskhod*. We know now the reason for this: in external appearance the *Voskhod* is indistinguishable from the *Vostok*. That is what makes the censor's mistake so amusing and so instructive, because he permitted the biographer to quote Korolyov's question just as it was spoken—with the word 'sphere' in it. When the biographer describes the *Voskhod* he keeps strictly to the official lie and the official fog. He says: 'This space-craft, which developed further all the best that was in the *Vostok* craft, went in many respects much further than they did. In it the astronauts were able [sic] for the first time to carry out a flight without space-suits. Nor was there any ejection mechanism, because the craft was to make a soft landing. New instruments, television and radio equipment were introduced.'

The last sentence can scarcely have its equal in the library of technological misinformation. It is remarkable for the fact that, strictly speaking, it corresponds to the truth. It is true that some radio equipment was actually introduced into the *Voskhod* which had not been aboard the *Vostok*. But this statement simply required a couple of qualifications. In the first place, the new instruments were miniaturised and had been specially purchased abroad in order to reduce the

131

weight of the radio equipment to an absolute minimum. In the second place, they were 'introduced' *in place of* all the *Vostok*'s instrumentation and *in place of* the supplies necessary for sustaining life on board the craft. In the *Vostok* the astronaut had a supply of everything necessary for him to survive for ten days; in the *Voskhod* there was only a three-day supply for the three astronauts and provision was made for them to have a full diet for only 24 hours. As the Russian writer Leonov once remarked: 'The best kinds of lies are prepared from half-truths . . .'

The parachute tests of the *Voskhod* with animals aboard were continued. In an effort to reduce the weight of the parachutes they were made from a thinner, synthetic material called kapron. Its resistance to the passage of air was very high, so that the landings were reasonably 'soft', but, on the other hand, the shock caused by the braking effect when the parachutes opened was very much more violent. So much so, in fact, that there was then thought to be a danger that the parachutes might be ripped away in the course of such a violent opening, and steps had to be taken to strengthen the lugs by which they were attached to the capsule. Korolyov and Voskresensky compensated for the additional weight involved in this modification by getting rid of a lot of explosive bolts, because it was no longer necessary to have the exit hatch shot off in flight.

Three months before it was due to be launched the *Voskhod* still weighed 100 kilograms (220 lbs) more than a standard *Vostok* rocket was capable of lifting. Then a real hunt began at the institute for every gram of weight that could be saved, even to the point of putting the appointed astronauts on a special diet consisting of a great deal of fruit, vegetables and meat but with practically no starch or fats in it. After the flight the doctors found all three astronauts in very good form, so that the diet had apparently served a double purpose. But it proved necessary to order the necessary foodstuffs, such as fillet steaks, fresh fish and various forms of fruit and juices and so forth, through a 'closed' government food store, because that year Khrushchev was obliged to buy even wheat from abroad.

Despite all these obstacles, by October 1964 the launching weight of the *Voskhod* space-craft had been reduced to a tolerable level—5,320 kilograms (11,704 lbs). That was the limit of what a *Vostok* rocket could lift into space if it used up the whole of its supply of fuel.

Khrushchev's Last Message

In the final months of his rule Nikita Khrushchev was in a constant state of gloom and depression. This is confirmed by everyone who met him at the time. I was among those who had such a meeting.

In the months of August and September 1964 an international building machinery exhibition was set up in the Luzhniki sports stadium in Moscow. I was sent by my magazine *Znaniye-Sila* to cover the whole exhibition. It had become the custom by that time for such exhibitions to receive an official visit just before it closed from the 'leaders of the Party and Government' headed by Khrushchev himself. For the last week of the exhibition, we journalists were obliged to remain on the spot the whole time, because nobody could tell at which moment the important visitors would turn up and we had to be careful not to miss so important an occasion. Many of the foreign correspondents also spent a lot of time at the exhibition's press centre waiting for the same occasion, although they usually do not put in an appearance at such shows.

On several occasions the words went round the press centre that 'they're on their way', and in fact a large detachment of the Kremlin's plain-clothes guard—the

133

'grey hats', as we used to call them among ourselves—appeared at the stadium more than once. But after hanging around for an hour or two they would suddenly depart, which meant that the visit had been cancelled at the last moment.

This continued until the last day of the exhibition—6 September. To our great surprise Khrushchev still did not appear, although there were two false alarms that day too. But just before the exhibition closed we were told that we should come to the exhibition on the morning of the next day, when it would already be shut to the public. The people manning the exhibition were given the same instructions.

We turned up as instructed at eight in the morning and hung around waiting. At eleven o'clock the 'grey hats' descended on the quiet, deserted exhibition ground to be followed almost immediately by Khrushchev himself. He was not accompanied by Brezhnev or Kosygin or Suslov or Podgorny, but only by Novikov, his deputy for building work and a few ministers.

I had already come into contact with Khruschchev on many occasions. I had first set eyes on him many years previously, in 1936, when I had been a 12-year-old Pioneer and Khrushchev was head of the Moscow organisation of the Communist Party. On that occasion I was chosen to lead him round the newly opened children's playground in the Krasnaya Presnya district and I was rewarded by a very warm embrace. This is not intended to suggest any personal acquaintance with the man, but it does mean that I was very well acquainted with the appearance and behaviour of Khrushchev in his encounters with other people.

But I had never seen Khrushchev look glum or behave so crudely as on 7 September 1964. Contrary to his usual manner he did not smile once throughout his tour of the exhibition. And when some exhibition employee forced his way up to him with a personal

134

letter (in accordance with the view still held by people in the Soviet Union that a request handed over personally to the leader will be satisfied) Khrushchev would not even take the envelope but shouted angrily: 'Get the hell out of it, you scoundrel! I've come here to do a job, and you want to shove bits of paper at me!' After which the unfortunate man was grabbed by the 'grey hats' who proceeded to find out who he was and what he wanted.

I was not alone in the impression I had of Khrushchev that day. I knew many of the journalists who always worked closely with Khrushchev and they were unanimous in asserting that until he went off to relax on the Black Sea coast at the end of September 1964 he was absolutely unbearable. From this one can have a good idea of the sort of talking-to Korolyov had from him since it was just before Khrushchev left for the Caucasus that he was summoned to report on the state of preparations for the space flight.

On the morning of 12 October 1964, a coach transported the pilot-astronaut Vladimir Komarov, the flight engineer Konstantin Feoktistov and the young doctor Boris Yegorov to the base of the 38-metre-(123 foot) high rocket. The astronauts were dressed in lightweight underwear. After an exchange of official greetings Korolyov went up to them and embraced each of them. He had never done such a thing on any previous occasion.

This rather unusual display of emotion was immediately given an official explanation. It was pointed out that all the earlier astronauts had been dressed up in their space-suits at that moment and that it was awkward and even rather ridiculous to embrace a man in a space-suit. Perhaps that was the explanation . . .

The astronauts managed one at a time to squeeze themselves into the capsule and for the first time at a space launching pulled the hatch shut behind them

135

from inside. Their predecessors had always been 'screwed in' from outside with special tools which measured the tension on the explosive bolts. On this occasion there were no such bolts.

The rocket motors worked without a hitch, the 'sphere' went into orbit, and 24 hours later, after completing 17 circuits of the Earth—according to the same programme as *Vostok-2* and the dogs had flown—it returned safely to earth. Once again another 'first' had been snatched from the Americans—the first group flight. What did it matter that in the next two years American astronauts made ten group flights, that they learnt to manoeuvre, to dock while in orbit, to leave the space ship in outer space and to remain outside it for two hours at a time! What did it matter that not one of the *Gemini* flights was the same as the preceding one and that each flight had to carry out and in fact carried out fresh and more difficult tasks! In spite of this the Soviet press and a certain section of the Western press continued to assert that the Russians were ahead, because in 1964 they had sent three astronauts into space, whereas there were only two men in the cockpits of the *Gemini* space-craft.

During the flight of the *Voskhod* its occupants spoke over the radio telephone to Khrushchev, according to the established custom. These pointless conversations, during which the astronauts would say no more than 'Yes, Nikita Sergeyevich' or 'Exactly, Nikita Sergeyevich' or 'Thank you, Nikita Sergeyevich' had long become the target of malicious jokes in the Soviet Union. On this occasion the telephone conversation turned out to be rather different from previous ones. In the first place, Khrushchev was not talking to the astronauts from Moscow but from his villa on the Black Sea. In the second place, Mikoyan also said a few words into the telephone. ('Anastas Ivanovich is

136

pulling the receiver out of my hand,' Khrushchev told the spacemen.) In the third place it was Khrushchev's last public statement.

On 13 October 1964 the *Voskhod* landed not far from Kustanai in Central Asia. The next day, 14 October, Khrushchev was summoned urgently to Moscow and was taken from the aerodrome where he arrived straight at the offices of the Central Committee of the Communist Party. The whole Central Committee was already in session there and Khrushchev was immediately informed of its decision to remove him from all his positions in the Party and the Government.

The Arrival

Next day, the 15th, the astronauts were due to come to Moscow for their official reception. But they did not arrive that day, nor the next, nor the next. Khrushchev's successors obviously had no time to bother with them, and the 'little eagles' were kept waiting in Central Asia until they received their instructions. It finally became impossible to hold things up further and it was decided that for Brezhnev and Kosygin to make their first public appearance as the new leadership at the official reception of the astronauts would not be a bad device. And so the ceremony took place, although a week later than planned.

There can be no doubt but that the great majority of the population of the Soviet Union followed the three-man flight with interest and appreciation. Nobody, of course, knew anything of what had been going on behind the scenes. Nevertheless, the fact that the astronauts had to be received by Brezhnev and Kosygin when, only a week previously they had spoken like loyal subjects to Khrushchev, who had in the meantime become an 'irresponsible voluntarist', had something of the operetta about it and provided material for a very biting anecdote which received wide currency throughout the Soviet Union.

It was the custom for all astronauts to end their formal speech at such ceremonies with the words: 'Ready to carry out any task set us by the Government'. The story went that on this occasion they finished up with the words: 'Ready to carry out the task set us by any Government'.

The flight of the *Voskhod* did not, of course, produce any significant scientific results. During the first days after the flight the Soviet press started to celebrate as a special achievement the fact that the astronauts had flown without space-suits. The implication was that the Soviet space-craft had been made so reliable that there was no longer any need for the astronauts to wear space-suits. But Korolyov demanded that there should be no more talk of the spacemen's underwear and his demand was accepted. In his biography we still find a reference to what they were wearing (in the passage describing the *Voskhod* quoted above), but it is no longer cited as an achievement. And in the *Soviet Encyclopaedia of Space Flight* published in 1969 there is no reference at all to the fact that the *Voskhod* crew did not wear space-suits. Moreover, on that page of the encyclopaedia (p. 493 of the English edition) where the *Voskhod* is described there is a photograph of the astronaut Leonov—in a space-suit! The photograph does not in fact relate to the article about the *Voskhod*, but the fact that it was printed on that page, and not on the next one, as it should have been, is in itself not unamusing.

When it came to describing the scientific results of the *Voskhod* flight, even the Soviet sources of information, usually so given to invention, found it beyond them. We come across phrases like 'a new multi-seater spaceship was tested in flight' or 'the capacity of astronauts specialised in various branches of science

138

and technology to work together was tried out'. The presence of the doctor, Yegorov, abroad the *Voskhod* provided the excuse for saying that 'an extensive programme of medico-biological research was carried out'. But the most remarkable description of the results of the *Voskhod* flight is to be found in the biography of Korolyov, in which there is not a word about 'medico-biological research' or about 'trying out the capacity to work together'. What it does say, however, is: 'A great deal was derived from observations of the Earth, space and heavenly bodies from the cockpit'.

Voskresensky Goes

As I pointed out at the very beginning of this book, with Khrushchev's departure from the scene Korolyov, Voskresensky and their colleagues began to have new hopes. They drew up a long report setting out in full detail the space-flight situation in the Soviet Union and the United States. They also described in great detail the story of how the *Voskhod* was prepared which, it is said, made a great impression on Brezhnev and Kosygin. It appeared to them as yet another typical example of Khrushchev's 'voluntarism' which they had finally revolted against.

Korolyov's report contained a number of proposals. Firstly, he proposed that they should drop all plans for a Moon-landing and carry out further research into the Moon's surface only within the limits of their own possibilities, which meant sending only small automatic instruments to the Moon. Secondly, he proposed that they should halt all flights for the moment and no longer try to overtake each of the forthcoming flights planned by the Americans under the *Gemini* programme. Thirdly, he suggested that they should set about developing, without the usual rush, a rocket-vehicle for the *Soyuz* space-craft, launch it and test the possibility

139

of setting up orbital space research stations. Fourthly, he proposed developing a shuttle-craft for relieving the people who would man the space stations.

These proposals were agreed with apparent goodwill by the new Soviet leaders. Pleased by this, Korolyov promised them in return that he would try after all to overtake the Americans in another sphere—in letting an astronaut leave the spaceship in outer space. It was known that on the first piloted *Gemini* flight the American astronauts were due to open their hatch and depressurise their cockpit, after which they were to seal it again and restore the internal pressure once more. On the second *Gemini* flight, shortly after the first one, it was planned that one of the astronauts should go for a walk in space. It was this American timetable, announced in advance as usual, that Korolyov proposed to beat by sending the 'sphere' on another flight and with exactly the same programme as that followed by the *Voskhod* and before it by the *Vostok-2* and before that by the dogs.

This proposal was, of course, also accepted and the staff of the institute set urgently about the task of building the space-craft. The rocket was already finished and ready for launching.

It was decided on Voskresensky's advice not to depressurise the capsule in flight. Instead a simpler idea was adopted : a light tube was attached to the hatch of the space-craft to form an exit-chamber into which the astronaut had to crawl before opening the outside hatch, which he did after the second astronaut had closed the inside hatch behind him. Re-entry into the space-craft was carried out by the reverse process. On the actual flight this system almost cost Alexei Leonov his life and was never used again on future flights.

Work on the modified capsule with room for the two astronauts and the exit chamber was interrupted

140

by the death of Voskresensky. He went on working right up to the last week of his life and even continued to take an interest in what was going on as he lay in hospital. He could not believe at the age of 52 that the end was near, but in fact he had only hours to live. Years spent in gaol, decades of unrelieved, exhausting labour and a constant state of nervous tension—this was what brought this exceptionally gifted man to his grave.

It was quite clear that Voskresensky's death was the last straw for Korolyov. In his last year of life nothing any longer was capable of cheering him up. At his deputy's graveside Korolyov said that had it not been for Voskresensky the first sputnik would not have been launched before the Americans launched theirs.

The First Space-Walk

Literally the day after the funeral Korolyov was again obliged to resume work at full stretch although he felt himself to be physically in very bad shape. A report was received that the *Gemini* spaceship was to be launched on 23 March. The Russian launching had at all costs to take place before that date. Khrushchev was no longer in the Kremlin, and the new men did not keep chasing Korolyov with telephone calls and urgent summonses, but the awareness that whatever happened and by whatever means the launching had to take place at least a day sooner than the Americans remained with Korolyov as strong as ever. Such was the effect of the psychological inertia which to this very day plays such a tremendous role in life in the Soviet Union.

Work on the *Voskhod-2*, as the spaceship was called, also involved solving a great many weighty problems. Two astronauts in spacesuits did not weigh very much less than three of them in their underwear. Apart from

141

THE RUSSIAN SPACE BLUFF

that there was the exit chamber which had not been attached to the previous craft. True, it was not possible to reduce still further the supplies carried on board for maintaining life: oxygen sufficient for two and a half days, food and water for two days, and all for two people. Cutting down the weight of the spaceship took a lot of time, especially since Voskresensky was no longer there to help with his stream of ideas. Less than a month was left for testing the ship.

The men chosen to make up the crew of *Voskhod-2* were Pavel Belyaev and Alexei Leonov, who had at one time been a candidate for the role of Astronaut No. 1. He was a very agile, athletic man, an outstanding parachutist and a competent pilot. Apart from all that, he was quite a good artist. He had to learn how to crawl out through the exit chamber and in fact, a week after he started his training he had mastered this operation and could perform it blindfold in just one minute.

The *Voskhod-2* spaceship lifted off at 10 a.m. on 18 March five days before the flight of *Gemini-3* manned by Grissom and Young. The Soviet radio announced with a great fanfare that the space-craft had been launched and had gone into orbit, but even then nothing was said about the purpose of the flight. And it was only after Leonov had left the capsule that a special announcement was made about it. Whether Khrushchev was there or not, the precautionary secrecy still remained.

It was about an hour later that the announcement was made that Leonov had returned to the cockpit of the space-craft, although only about 20 minutes elapsed from the time the exit hatch was opened to the moment it was pulled down again. The fact was that those were very dramatic minutes.

Leonov extracted himself from the capsule without anything going wrong. Once the astronaut was outside

142

the spaceship Korolyov made contact with him by radio. After nine minutes of walking in space Leonov was instructed to return to the spaceship. But, as it turned out, this was not easy to accomplish.

In the course of the few minutes Leonov spent in outer space his space-suit expanded like a balloon. This was the result of the so-called 'football bladder effect' which had been correctly anticipated by English experts and taken into account by the Americans. If it had not been for Alexei Leonov's exceptional agility he would never have succeeded in squeezing himself back into the entry chamber. As I said, he had carried out this operation in the course of his training in one minute with his eyes closed. Now, with his eyes open, it took him eight minutes to force his way in and throughout this time his comments were picked up in his microphone: 'I can't . . .I can't . . . Again I can't make it . . . I'll have another go . . . No, again I can't get in . . . I can't!' When he finally managed to squeeze through the hatch Leonov let out a loud 'Hurrah!' and released the tension by some lengthy curses.

Into the Snow

That was not, however, the last mishap in the course of the flight. On the seventeenth circuit of the Earth the same thing happened as had happened twice before in 1960 with the unmanned capsules: the braking motor system—the TDU—did not switch on at the signal from ground control. Korolyov ordered them to prepare to switch the TDU on manually at a signal given by word of mouth after the following eighteenth circuit. Here was where Korolyov's foresight came into play. All the capsules, including the very first in which Gagarin flew, were equipped with the means of operating the TDU by hand. Not one of the astronauts in the *Vostok* space-craft had made use

143

of it, and there were those who considered that the hand operation mechanism was an unnecessary luxury. Yet on the eighth of the manned flights it was unexpectedly found to be essential and in fact saved the lives of two astronauts.

After the eighteenth circuit it was impossible to bring the space-craft down in the southern half of the Soviet Union, only in the northern part. All air force units stationed in the Far North and the Arctic regions were immediately informed what was likely to happen in an area which was still wrapped in deep winter with sub-zero temperatures and very deep snow. When he received the signal Belyaev switched on the TDU instantly, but said at once that, although the TDU had come into action, he was not sure about the orientation. Happily the orientation was correct. The *Voskhod-2* landed in deep snow covering a sparse forest near Perm. It was seen by the local inhabitants, who reported the landing to the nearest military unit. Thanks to this piece of good fortune the rescue team were with Belyaev and Leonov a few hours after they landed.

Official Soviet accounts of space flights make no reference whatsoever to these two extraordinary events which took place aboard the *Voskhod-2*. It was simply announced (as a major achievement, of course) that, as command-pilot of *Voskhod-2*, Belyaev brought the TDU system into play manually. And it was only much later, about a year after the flight had taken place, that it was said in passing that the space-craft was not brought down in the usual landing area but 2,000 kilometres (1,250 miles) to the north of it, and that the flight did not last the usual 24 hours and a few minutes but 26 hours. Finally, in Korolyov's biography both these incidents are presented in a very forced 'light', almost slapstick manner. Concerning Leonov's efforts to get back into the spaceship the biographer lets fall incidentally just one sentence: 'He didn't

144

succeed in getting into the entry chamber at the first try.' He didn't succeed: that was all, without any further explanation. As for the second mishap, this is dealt with in the biography in the following passage:

'As we know, the *Voskhod-2* spaceship was the first one to be brought down manually, without using the automatic piloting system.

"Now chaps, have a go at doing it manually," the ground flight controller, Yuri Gagarin, told them with Korolyov's approval.

So they made yet another circuit of the Earth. Then they lined up the spaceship manually and brought the braking system into action.

There was a terrific noise aboard the spaceship. Where would it go now? Supposing they had not lined it up correctly and it was not aiming at the Earth but away from it?

But then they could tell by the specks of dust that were falling that everything was in order and that the spaceship was passing through the denser layers of the Earth's atmosphere.'

It was possible to claim that the flight of *Voskhod-2* unlike the flights which had preceeded it, had achieved an appreciable scientific result: a man had walked in space for the first time. The Medical examination revealed that Leonov had withstood his walk very well. But P. Belyaev was less fortunate: when I was already in Britain I learnt from Soviet newspapers that he had died from some internal illness at the age of 37. But what exactly had killed him was not said.

The *Voskhod-2* was the last manned space ship to be launched in the Soviet Union in Sergei Korolyov's lifetime. Ten months after its flight, on 15 January 1966, the great engineer died in hospital. His ailing heart came to a halt, unable to sustain an operation for the removal of a cancerous tumour.[1]

[1] When this book was already at the printers a Yugoslav publishing house produced in Russian the reminiscences of Professor G. A. Ozerov who was held from 1938 to 1941 in the "special prison" attached to factory No. 156 along with A. N. Tupolev and S. P. Korolyov. These reminiscences were written in Moscow and circulated for some time in a clandestine "samizdat" version before finding their way to Yugoslavia. They add many interesting details to what we already know about the years which Korolyov spent in prison.

In the first place Ozerov asserts that, before being transferred to the "privileged" prison to work with Tupolev, Sergi Korolyov spent some time as an ordinary prisoner in a prison camp in the Kolyma goldfields, a place from which very few people ever returned. Tupolev himself mentioned Korolyov's name when he was invited, following his arrest, to draw up a list of people who might work along with him. I was not aware of this fact when I was writing the book.

Next, Professor Ozerov confirms that when he was in the special prison with Tupolev, Korolyov worked on wing design. (It will be recalled that, without mentioning his arrest, Korolyov's official biography does say that in 1939 and 1940 Korolyov was the wing designer under Tupolev.) Ozerov's reminiscences also confirm the fact that, after the special prison was evacuated to Omsk, Korolyov was transferred from Tupolev's work to Moscow, to work in the "special prison" where rockets were being developed. But Ozerov, who had never been in that prison, says it was attached to the "Ilyich" factory, and not in the place indicated in my book.

The main value of Professor Ozerov's reminiscences lies, however, in the additional information he provides about the appearance and character of the future Chief Design Engineer of space craft. He describes Korolyov in these words:

"Short of stature, heavily built, his head sitting awkwardly on his body, with brown eyes glistening with intelligence, he was a sceptic, a cynic and a pessimist who took the gloomiest view of the future. 'We will all vanish without a trace' was his favourite expression."

Ozerov continued to meet Korolyov after he became Chief Design Engineer. "Though he had been elevated to the greatest heights of flattery, orders, titles, esteem and so forth, he did not abandon his old friends. The most fascinating times were when, at Kalinin's former country house near Ostankino, over a glass of brandy, after glancing over his shoulder he would drop his voice to a whisper and start reminiscing: 'Do you remember the time when we . . .' "

According to Ozerov, Korolyov spoke in the following terms: "You know, my friends, the real tragedy is that they do not understand how much life today has in common with what it was then. I can still not get away from the thought of 'vanishing without a trace'. Sometimes I wake up at night and lie there thinking: at any moment the order might be given and the very same guards could burst in and shout: 'Come on, scum, get your things together and on your way!' "

Ozerov adds that the similarity with earlier days was underlined by the fact that the guard on Korolyov's country house was manned by exactly the same sort of warders as had been at the Tupolev prison. Ozerov also says that Korolyov did not die from an operation for cancer, as was then reported in Moscow, but from one for haemorrhoids, and suggests that the Kremlin doctors did not make the best job of the operation. I can only add that the immediate cause of death was the state of Korolyov's heart following the operation.

146

PART FOUR

THE SETTING OF THE SUN

Research in Fetters

After the flight in March 1965 of the *Voskhod-2* with Belyaev and Leonov aboard the Soviet Union did not undertake any manned spaceflights for more than two years. Then, on 23 April 1967, a *Soyuz* spaceship was sent up on a test flight. This craft was, as we know, the brainchild of the two great designers, both of whom were now dead, Korolyov and Voskresensky, and had been ready for launching as far back as the end of 1963. It was actually launched in April 1967 because by that time a more powerful vehicle had been developed for it. The vehicle was again powered by a multichamber engine arranged in a cluster. In so far as the cluster arrangement was Korolyov's idea it may be said that the launching of the *Soyuz* was his work.

Unfortunately he was no longer present to supervise the preparations for the flight as he had supervised all the earlier ones, and there was no one to replace him in the workshops and to look into every little detail with his unique and special knowledge of the business and his ability to foresee possible snags. On the other hand, the systematic checking of each component of the rocket before launching by means of computers, which has long been the rule in America, is even

147

today not the practice in the Soviet Union. As a result *Soyuz 1*, launched either as a precaution or to save weight with only one astronaut aboard, ran into disaster and was lost.

The man selected to be the pilot of the *Soyuz-1* was the best educated and most skilful of the Soviet astronauts, Vladimir Komarov. He was the first of them to make a second trip into outer space, and his second flight proved fatal for him.

Very little is known about the causes of the loss of *Soyuz-1* and Vladimir Komarov. The official Soviet account says simply that after 24 hours in flight the spaceship entered the denser layers of the Earth's atmosphere as planned, but that at a height of 7,000 metres (23,000 feet) the main parachutes failed to operate and the *Soyuz* was destroyed.

This account of what happened seems to me more than doubtful. What puzzles me most is the length of the flight—24 hours. That means that it consisted once again of only 17 orbits of the Earth, exactly the same as with the flights with the dogs, with *Vostok-2*, *Voskhod-1* and *Voskhod-2*. But what reason could there have been to repeat that old schedule, which Korolyov had resorted to only very reluctantly and out of necessity and which he had almost been ashamed of? There was, after all a perfectly good explanation for the 24-hour flights of the *Voskhods*: their capsules were overloaded, with three people in the first one and two in the second. For that reason a long flight had been unthinkable because the supplies of food, oxygen, water and so forth were extremely limited. Seventeen orbits were, as we know, the smallest number after which the capsule was in a position for being brought down in a suitable area.

But none of these reasons applied to the length of flight in the case of *Soyuz-1*. In the capsule which was more spacious than the earlier ones there was only one

148

astronaut. Even if by that time the rocket vehicle had not been powerful enough to put a much bigger load into the *Soyuz* it was still unlikely to carry a supply of nourishment for less than ten days. After all, even the *Voskhod-1* had a three-day supply of oxygen for three people, that is to say enough for one man for nine days. So it was obviously not the reserves of nourishment which limited Komarov's flight to 24 hours.

On the other hand, we know now that the first successful *Soyuz* flight, carried out 18 months after the Komarov disaster, lasted for four days, also with just one astronaut aboard. It is difficult to believe, therefore, that the 1967 flight was for some reason intended to last only 24 hours. After all, by that time the Americans had carried out ten *Gemini* flights one after the other and some of the *Gemini* craft had stayed in space for weeks. Even if Komarov's flight was not intended, unlike the earlier ones, to establish yet another 'first' in space, it surely had to mark some kind of step forward.

For all these reasons I find it extremely difficult to believe that Komarov's timetable provided for him to return to Earth after 24 hours. If I am right in this, and the flight was intended to last longer, then the story of the parachutes failing to open put forward by Soviet sources does not hold water. Then Komarov's attempt to bring the flight to an end prematurely must have been due to something that went wrong abroad the spaceship, the nature of which we can only guess at.

The cause of Komarov's death has, of course, no direct connection with the story I have to tell. But the disaster was a very unhappy experience for me personally because I met Vladimir Komarov and had great respect for him. Unlike the other pilots with relatively little education and limited intelligence, such as Gagarin, Nikolayev, Popovich, Bykovsky, and Tereshkova, Komarov was a very intelligent man and in addition,

149

to judge by my very superficial impression of him, a good and kind man.

The Delay and the Gap

It was hardly surprising that the *Soyuz-1* disaster delayed further launchings in the Soviet Union by eighteen months. Accidents of that kind always have similar consequences. The tragedy at Cape Kennedy on 27 January 1967, when three astronauts died as a result of a fire on the spaceship, delayed the carrying out of the *Apollo* programme by roughly the same period of time. But even if Komarov's flight in April 1967 had not ended tragically the extent by which the Soviet Union was lagging behind the United States in the field of space flight would have been just as enormous. At that time the Soviet Union had yet to repeat (goodness knows why) the varied programme of space experiments which had been carried out on the ten *Gemini* flights, and with a very precise aim in view—a landing on the Moon. But the Soviet scientists are still (i.e. in December 1970, after the Soviet *lunokhod* had been placed on the Moon) a long way from completing the volume of work carried out on the *Gemini* flights on orbits round the Earth. Incidentally, the last of the *Gemini* series of flights took place in November 1966. If we then recall the subsequent *Apollo* programme, in the course of which three groups of American astronauts landed on the Moon the contrast is even clearer, since the Soviet Union has simply not been able to attempt anything resembling that feat.

I hope the reader will by now be able to understand what I felt when I came to talk with a London publisher at the end of 1966. By that time the Americans had already completed their *Gemini* programme, while the Soviet Union had not even started on it. Preparations for the *Apollo* programme were going at full speed in

150

America, while my Soviet scientist friends could not even dream of beginning to plan any programme of that kind. Yet none of my arguments were capable of moving that publisher, who went on believing blindly that the Russians would still be the first to reach the Moon!

In the years I have now spent in Britain the question has frequently been put to me: how do you explain the fact that the Russians have fallen behind in the space race? Perhaps the new leaders who came to power after Khrushchev decided to distribute their resources in a more cautious manner? Better informed people wondered whether Korolyov's death had had an effect on the course of Soviet space research. But behind all these questions there was always the same basic query: why on earth had the Soviet Union 'lost' its leadership in space and allowed the Americans to get in front?

I hope that now, after what I have written, the true position will be clear: that the Russians were *never* ahead in space. There had been only the appearance of leadership: shows brilliantly staged by a great producer, Korolyov, to scripts provided by the Americans. Even he could not, of course, have long continued putting on such shows; without him they were bound to come to an end at once. What the Soviet Union is doing in space today leaves a very painful impression.

I have already said in the course of this book, but I shall repeat it here because of its importance, that the Soviet Union's backwardness in space research is perfectly natural and inevitable, because the Soviet Union is a backward country and in particular is a technologically backward country. What was *not* natural or inevitable was the emergence of the Soviet Union on to the space scene, but, as I have explained, this was in fact an attempt on the part of a man of genius to be far ahead of his time. A genius can, after all, always move ahead of his time in any field of human endeavour.

It may be said that the Soviet Union is not only

151

engaged in space research but also possesses nuclear bombs of enormous power as well as intercontinental ballistic missiles, atomic submarines and a vast number of modern aircraft. It would, however, be a mistake to judge the country's technological level by reference to these items.

Thanks to a rigid and unrestrained dictatorship the Soviet rulers are able to direct whatever resources and efforts they wish to the achievement of specific, limited objectives. One such narrow aim of the Soviet régime always was and remains today to be first in the arms race. More than half of all Soviet industrial enterprises are engaged entirely on the production or development of armaments; many of the remaining factories are carrying out various kinds of military contracts, occasionally or regularly. When I was working in a motor-car factory in Moscow, for example, we produced apart from small passenger cars, starting motors for the engines of military aircraft and telephone instruments for military field communications, both under the supervision of a special representative from the war department. Yet that factory was regarded as a completely 'open' enterprise and not in the least secret, and it was often visited by foreigners. I myself occasionally conducted foreign guests round the factory, carefully avoiding the section where the military material was being assembled. To tell the truth there was in fact no likelihood of my going into that section by mistake, because there was a guard stationed at it and entry was possible only to people with a special stamp on their factory passes.

With such a concentration of resources and effort in one direction, and at the expense of the standard of living of the people as a whole, it is possible, of course, to achieve a great deal, especially in a country so rich in natural resources as is the Soviet Union. Nevertheless the Soviet Union suffers from technological backwardness even in the field of armaments. It is, after all, no accident that the Soviet authorities have set up such a vast network of spies throughout the world at such enormous expense. The Soviet atomic bomb was partly the work of Bruno Pontecorvo, the atomic physicist who was lured from the West, and the spying performed by Klaus Fuchs, Colonel Abel and others. The Soviet nuclear bomb was partly the work of the Rosenbergs and their accomplices, and the Soviet atomic submarines owe much to the work of Gordon Lonsdale, the Krogers and other Soviet agents.

Only in the field of rocketry was the situation in the Soviet Union somewhat better than in other fields, because here it is possible to speak of a certain tradition and of the 'school' of Zander and Korolyov. But here too, of course, foreign experience and foreign engineering exerted a great influence. It is sufficient to recall the German experts who were transported to the Soviet Union after the Second World War and to mention the name of Yangel, who still occupies one of the very highest positions in the Soviet rocket hierarchy. Apart from that the Soviet Union continues to carry on very active espionage work in that field, as was revealed by the stealing of a *Sidewinder* rocket in Western Germany and its transfer to the Eastern part of the country.

The one-sided development of Soviet industry in favour of armaments production costs the country and its population very dearly. A State which knows well how to make rockets and bombs has found it impossible to organise satisfactorily its own motor-car production. All the Soviet cars manufactured in the last half-century have been in one way or the other of foreign origin. Even more hopelessly behind the times are such branches of Soviet industry as those producing plastics, artificial fibres, chemical fertilisers and weed-killers. In no part of the country do they produce good quality clothes, decent footwear or even more or less

153

presentable paper. Despite the vast areas of fertile land and the extremely low density of population (no more than 11 people to the square kilometre—26 to the square mile) the supply even of bread to the population depends entirely on the harvest in each successive year. If there is a poor harvest, the country finds itself on the verge of starvation and has to use its natural reserves of gold, timber, furs and other valuable raw materials to purchase grain from abroad.

Because he had at his disposal excellent assistants and unlimited resources, and because he was himself a brilliant engineer, Sergei Korolyov succeeded even in such conditions of technological backwardness to achieve what he did—to put spaceship-satellites into orbit round the Earth. But to organise, say, the flight of a man to the Moon requires technological equipment of such variety and complexity that, even if Korolyov were alive today, he would scarcely be likely to take on such a task. It is no accident that, according to his official biography, Korolyov devoted a great deal of thought in the last months of his life to writing a book on rocketry, in which 'Sergei Pavlovich proposed to devote special attention to describing interplanetary orbital stations and other ideas for enabling man to remain for prolonged periods in outer space.'

Knowing about the American *Apollo* project—it had already been announced in all its details in 1965— Korolyov saw that the Soviet Union's only alternative was to construct orbital stations. It was at least possible to cherish real hopes of carrying out such a plan. So far, however, it has not proved possible to realise even those modest hopes of Sergei Korolyov.

What's Going On?

The space launchings which have taken place in the Soviet Union since the death of Sergei Korolyov have

154

been marked by the lack of any clear plan behind them, an excessive sensitivity on the part of the authorities and a relative lack of success. The first successful flight of a *Soyuz* space-ship in October 1968 lasted for four days, in the course of which the only astronaut on board, Georgi Beregovoi, tried to come together with the second unmanned *Soyuz*. This took place two and a half years after Neil Armstrong had carried out the first docking in space with an unmanned space-craft. What is more, this experiment, in the course of which a dramatic situation developed requiring the rapid 'un-docking' of the two craft, had been described at great length in documents which, it must be presumed, were carefully studied by the Soviet experts. Nevertheless, Beregovoi did not succeed even in bringing his *Soyuz* craft close to the unmanned capsule.

It was not until January 1969 that the Soviet Union carried out a docking in space of two manned spaceships—the *Soyuz-4* and *Soyuz-5*. This was already three and a half years after the first American operation of the same kind and a month after the *Apollo-8* astronauts had returned from their orbit round the Moon. The Russians have still not repeated their attempt to dock manned space-craft, although in October 1969 (three months after the Americans had landed on the Moon) three *Soyuz* spacecraft were launched into space at intervals of 24 hours. All the Western experts took it for granted that the three spaceships would join up in space at last to form a space-station, while specialists in exaggerating Soviet space achievements and all newspapermen of an anti-American persuasion were anticipating some amazing new achievement about to be brought off by the Soviet Union. It was then, for example, that the London *Times* wrote that by putting three space-craft into orbit the Russians had performed a sort of revolution in space research. But, to the great disappointment of

155

all the badly informed well-wishers, each of the three *Soyuz* craft simply circled the Earth for five days and then returned without providing any surprises at all.

For 14 months after that event only one manned flight took place in the Soviet Union. Nikolayev, who had already experience of space flight, and another astronaut, Sevastyanov, completed a long but equally uneventful flight around the Earth in another *Soyuz* craft. But these operations did not approach in any sense the extent of the work carried out by American astronauts during the *Gemini* programme which was completed in 1966.

Nevertheless it cannot be said that the Soviet Union is now four years behind the United States in the field of space research. A comparison between the two countries in terms of 'specific achievements' is not a sure guide, as we have seen in the case of Korolyov's apparent success in 'overtaking' the Americans. The Soviet Union is not lagging behind the United States by four years but by a whole epoch, as was correctly pointed out by three Soviet scholars, A. Sakharov, R. Medvedev and V. Turchin, in their protest-letter published in 1970.

The American *Apollo* programme and the extraordinary interest which the Soviet population showed in the Moon landing caused the Soviet rulers serious concern. The Americans' 'invasion' of the Moon, coming less than a year after the Russians had invaded Czechoslovakia with their tanks, had a very unfavourable propaganda effect for the Soviet leaders. There can be no doubt that, even before the launching of *Apollo-11* the present Soviet space experts had received instructions to devise some way of minimising the effect of the American triumph. That accounted for the series of unmanned launchings which in fact did nothing to restore Soviet morale.

156

At the very same time as the *Apollo-11* expedition was setting off for the Moon the Soviet Union unexpectedly launched an unmanned Moon station, *Luna-15*. It went into orbit round the Moon just as Armstrong and Aldrin had carried out the first Moon landing in the history of mankind. The Soviet launching caused the American space authorities a certain concern, and people devised the most unlikely theories about the purpose behind the Russian automatic Moon station, some going as far as to suggest that it contained a secret weapon for destroying the *Apollo* craft. The American authorities even addressed an official enquiry to the Soviet Government through diplomatic channels and received a reply from the President of the Soviet Academy of Science, Professor M. Keldysh, to the effect that *Luna-15* would not interfere in any way with the work of the *Apollo* expedition. This turned out to be completely correct, because *Luna-15* struck the Moon far from the area where the *Apollo* module had landed and broke up on the Moon's surface. But what point there had been in launching *Luna-15* still remained unclear. The communique issued on the subject in the Soviet Union was couched in the usual vague phraseology, saying nothing more than that the *Luna-15* had 'carried out its programme of work'.

It was only more than a year later, when the next Soviet automatic station *Luna-16* arrived on the Moon, that the purpose of the previous launching became apparent. The fact was that *Luna-16* was equipped with an automatic device for collecting soil, which took a sample of the Moon's rocky surface weighing about 100 grams (less than four ounces), and a return module. The sample of Moon dust was automatically drawn into the module, measuring about a foot across, and returned to the Earth. The Soviet press then made a great deal of fuss, rather belatedly, about the advantages of exploring the Moon by means of automatic instruments without causing men to risk their lives at it.

There could then no longer be any doubt but that the purpose of *Luna-15*, launched quite shamelessly at the same time as *Apollo-11*, had been to obtain a sample of the Moon's surface and bring it back to the Earth. This would have given the Soviet propagandists the chance to set the Soviet achievement against the American and claim that the Russians had done more or less the same as the Americans but without using people to do it. It is also clear that the work had been carried out at the NII88 institute in the same feverish haste so as to launch the *Luna-15* exactly on time and that this caused a breakdown. It took them a whole year to prepare a successful flight of the same type.

But American launchings of the *Apollo* series are being carried out according to the timetable, and the authors of the Soviet space encyclopaedia do not even hesitate to publish the timetable in full, right up to the *Apollo-20* expedition (later cancelled), including the names of the astronauts and the places where they are to land. Even the accident that befell the *Apollo-13* turned into a sort of space triumph. And this was why the Soviet space scientists, the most honest of whom are surely blushing for shame, were ordered to think up some new tricks. The result of their efforts was the *lunokhod*, which was launched in November 1970.

An amusing aspect of this affair, which went quite unnoticed by Western journalists, was the fact that at no point in the course of the noisy press campaign around the *lunokhod* were the actual measurements of the machine given. All the photographs of this trolley driven by batteries powered by the Sun were taken in such a way as not to include any objects of known dimensions, such as plants, furniture or people. The journalists in Moscow were shown an enlarged

158

model of the *lunokhod* and got no answers to questions about its actual size. As a result of this even as experienced an observer as the British science writer Peter Fairley spoke in a programme on the London *Thames* television of 'the Russian *lunokhod*, about the size of the Mini motorcar'.

But it was quite clear to people familiar with the Soviet space programme that the *lunokhod* was a sort of self-propelled toy scarcely six feet long. That was in fact what it was, as became apparent in February 1971 when a Soviet scientific magazine quietly released details of its measurements.

There could be no doubt that the general structure and dimensions of *Luna-17* were the same as those of *Luna-16*. It was that which led me to my conclusion about the diminutive size of the *lunokhod*, which nevertheless provided the means of putting across yet another great bluff.

On the Decline

All the same, and despite the apparent eagerness of certain groups of people in the West to believe the reverse, we are now able to observe a decline in the effectiveness of the Soviet space bluff. I do not, of course, know what new tricks the people working in the field of space research in the Soviet Union will think up in order to 'maintain their reputation'. I only know that there will be more such tricks.

If we consider the question of the rockets used by the Russians, then it can be seen that the launching of *Luna-16* and *Luna-17*, as well as of the *Zond-6* and *Zond-7* space-stations which preceeded them and circled the Moon before returning to Earth, did not represent anything new even from the point of view of what the Soviet Union had already achieved. In fact, as far back as September 1959 Korolyov had gained

159

the Soviet Union another 'first' by sending to the Moon the *Luna-2* station which left metal plaques bearing the Soviet emblem and a portrait of Lenin on the surface of the Earth's only natural satellite. Strictly speaking, subsequent stations could have been despatched to the Moon by means of the very same rocket, although in all probability a different one was used, since 11 years had elapsed. We can be quite sure that the *Luna-16* and *Luna-17* stations were not very heavy, otherwise there would have been no good reason for the Soviet authorities to go to so much trouble to conceal their weight.

What was new in the launchings of *Luna-16* and *Luna-17* were the improved systems for communications and remote control, which made it possible for part of *Luna-16* to lift off automatically on its return journey to Earth and for the *Lunokhod* to move about the Moon's surface at signals from ground control. But this aspect of the affair is not directly connected with the advancement of Soviet space technology and shows only that the Soviet electronics specialists have succeeded recently in reducing the serious gap existing in this all important field between the Soviet Union and the United States. But the gap still exists and remains very large, in spite of the successful operation of the radio-controlled toy.

The Structure

My story would be incomplete and the reasons for Soviet successes and failures would remain unclear if I were not to give a more general account of the way scientific research is organised and functions in the Soviet Union and of the steps taken to preserve the secrecy of all scientific and technological work.

Scientific research in the Soviet Union is mainly concentrated, not in the universities as in America and some other countries, but in special organisations,

160

known as scientific-research institutions (NII). Applied scientific and technological development work also takes place mainly in special organisations—experimental design bureaus (OKB). It sometimes happens that one or other of these institutions will have attached to it an experimental factory which makes prototypes of the newly developed machines or instruments. Sometimes it is the other way round: a large factory may have its own OKB working on the development of experimental versions of future products.

As for the universities and other institutes of higher education, formally they are also centres of scientific research. But since the work has to be carried on by the very same teachers, undergraduates and post-graduates who are fully occupied on teaching courses and since no large sums are allotted for 'university science', no really important work in pure or applied science is done as a rule in the universities or higher institutes.

In the post-war period the Soviet authorities began setting up isolated scientific centres, far removed from any towns or other populated areas. They were called 'science towns'. The first place to become a town of this kind was the centre at which the Soviet atomic and nuclear bombs were developed, and where work on them continues to this day. Where this secret town is actually situated I do not know, although I have met many people who were working there. They all call this mysterious place 'Problema'. The town of Problema was founded by no less a person than the notorious Lavrenti Beria, the 'Soviet Himmler', head of Stalin's secret police and a man responsible for the deaths of untold thousands of innocent people, who was finally executed by his colleagues. Stalin entrusted Beria with the task of organising the manufacture of atomic bombs, a task which, generally speaking, Beria fulfilled.

161

The chief design engineer for nuclear weapons in the Soviet Union since the very beginning of work in that sphere is Academician Yuri Khariton, the best student and closest colleague of the late Academician Yoffe, one of the Soviet Union's leading scholars, but to all outside appearances a puny and undersized little man.

The town of Problema was also the place which saw the rising of another scientific star, the remarkable scientist Academician Andrei Sakharov who, after completing his studies at the Faculty of Physics at Moscow University only in 1945, rose rapidly to take charge of all work on the nuclear (hydrogen) bomb. Other outstanding scientists, such as Academicians Bogolyubov, Zeldovich and Weinstein, worked at Problema at various times.

The difficulties which had to be overcome in the production of the Soviet atomic and nuclear bombs were beyond belief—probably even more enormous than those which faced the rocket scientists. And it should not be thought that those difficulties were overcome only thanks to information obtained from the West by means of spies. After all, the equipment and all the machines which were required for the enrichment of uranium or obtaining lithium hydride or for other complex processes were not brought from the West. The people working at Problema were helped a great deal by the fact that the Soviet Union had inherited from pre-revolutionary times a very distinguished school of physicists, including such outstanding figures as Lebedev, Friedmann, Yoffe, Landau, Kapitsa, Fok and Tamm. They were also helped by having at their disposal the talents of the men who actually carried out the practical work— Khariton, Kurchatov, Sakharov and Bogolyubov. Finally the atomic scientists were provided with unlimited resources; any of the country's industrial plants could be put to work for them if necessary; and then they had the benefit of the activities of the whole Soviet spy network abroad.

A number of other science towns were set up apart from Problema, some of them also secret and some not. For example, Beria created the town of Dubna 80 miles north of Moscow. Until Stalin's death this town was secret. Physicists worked there on the acceleration of elementary particles and research into high energy particles. It was there that, after he had been lured to Russia from the West, Professor Pontecorvo was put to work. He was a former colleague of Enrico Fermi and along with him had set up the first atomic reactor in the United States. It was at Dubna that the great scientist Academician Veksler worked until his last days, and it is there that one of the discoverers of atomic fission, Academician Flerov, is still conducting research.

Around 1950 yet another secret science town was set up about 65 miles south-west of Moscow. That was Obninsk, where in 1954 under the direction of Academician Leipunsky an atomic reactor was built which provided steam for the turbines of a small electricity generating station of 5,000 kilowatts. That was the world's first atomic power station. Apart from that, Obninsk had an institute of physics and energetics and an institute of medical radiology.

In 1955 on Khrushchev's initiative the 'Siberian Section of the Soviet Academy of Science' was set up near Novosibirsk with the Ukrainian mathematician, Academician Mikhail Lavrentiev, in charge. The town now has more than forty thousand inhabitants, a university and a large number of research institutes. 'Akademgorodok', as it is known unofficially, receives a great number of foreign visitors and is known throughout the world. Nevertheless even in this 'open' science town there are a great many places and whole buildings with armed guards who prevent unauthorised people from entering and where secret research work of a military nature is carried on.

There are in the Soviet Union still other scientific centres consisting of whole towns which are still secret, which are not shown on any maps, which have no names but are known only by numbers. That is the status, for example, of the 'Baikonur space centre' near Tyuratam, the only postal address for which is 'Kzyl-Orda-50'.

All this looks very impressive. Nevertheless all branches of science, both pure and applied, in the Soviet Union advance very slowly, and the application of the results of scientific research to practical purposes takes place even more slowly. The progress of Soviet science is impeded by major defects inherent in the country's political system.

The Main Obstacles

There are four main defects, though there are many other, less important ones. The first is the continual and invariably harmful interference in scientific affairs on the part of political leaders with no under-standing of science; the second is the necessity under which scientists work to try and fit all their scientific conclusions—no matter what their branch of science—into the prevailing ideological framework of Marxism-Leninism; the third is the unbelievable conservatism and sluggishness inherent in the country's economic structure which results in a general fear of everything novel or of taking responsibility for possible failure; the fourth is the all-pervading secrecy.

Everything in the Soviet Union is centralised, in-cluding the 'leadership' of science. On the surface this appears simply to mean that all scientific research is coordinated and directed by the Soviet Academy of

Science. But that is only on the surface. In the first place, by no means all of the research institutes or experimental bureaus come under the Academy. A tremendous number of research institutes and the overwhelming majority of the experimental bureaus are outside the jurisdiction of the Academy. They 'belong' to all sorts of ministries, departments and committees. For example, the centres for research into atomic physics come under the Committee for Atomic Energy of the Soviet Council of Ministers, and the Majority of the experimental bureaus connected with those centres belong to the Ministry of Medium Engineering. Scientific institutes concerned with rocketry are dealt with by the Ministry of the Aircraft Industry and the Ministry of Defence. Secondly, there are two additional bureaucratic superstructures possessing enormous power—the Government's State Committee for Science and Technology and the Party Central Committee's Department of Science.

These two departments constitute a gigantic army of officials who, even if they were inspired by the very best of intentions, would still inevitably act as a brake on scientific progress. Moreover the decisive factor is not the intentions but the level of knowledge of the officials, and that remains depressingly low.

What the government departments demand above all from the scientific institutions is that they should draw up and submit for approval unending 'work plans' for the future. According to a long-standing Soviet tradition such plans must always indicate the benefit to be derived from the particular piece of development work once it is put into practice. But what can a scientist say in response to such a question? Until he starts work on a particular theme he is in a position to say no more than that the subject interests him; he does not even know whether the work will produce any worth-while results at all. But if a

165

scientist were to put that down in his plan no official in any department would approve it. Consequently he has to resort to using his imagination, and the work involved in drawing up far-fetched work plans and getting them approved in one department after another takes up an enormous amount of every scientist's time.

But however fantastic a plan may be it also has a certain effect, and a very negative one, on day to day work. The fact is that the officials in charge of scientific work do not simply sit in their offices and consume to no good purpose the enormous funds expended on them. They also go around visiting scientific institutes and demand that the plans are carried out. It is therefore not possible simply to draw up an unreal plan and then forget about it and get on with something else. You have as far as possible to organise things in such a way that the visiting inspectors do not start any trouble but go away with the impression that the plan is being fulfilled. Organising this kind of deception also takes a good deal of time, money and nervous energy.

An especially difficult situation develops when a scientist finds it necessary to concentrate his efforts on some abstract theme which does not promise to produce any immediate results. To obtain funds for work on such a subject is possible only if it is approved by higher authorities as part of the plan for the following year. The situation may not be too difficult if the subject is in some way connected with the possibility of being applied to military needs—for example, if it is connected with nuclear physics or the theory of masers or bacteriology. In that case it is possible at least to hint vaguely in the plan at the importance of the anticipated results for 'defence'. But if it is a matter of researching into the nature of the gene or, worse still, Sanskrit writings, then there is little hope. In that case the officials responsible for approving the

166

plan will immediately recall the importance of economising State funds, because as the principal squanderers of the country's wealth they always claim to be in favour of the strictest economy.

The most obvious result of such uninformed and illusory economies is, as I have said above, a very one-sided development of Soviet science and technology. A country which has plenty of rockets and bombs is still producing plastics, glass, rubber, medicines and paper of appallingly low quality and in hopelessly insufficient quantities. A country which has supersonic aircraft is hopelessly short of motor-cars and modern roads. The Soviet Union has built gigantic electric power stations, but there is no electricity in half the country's villages because of the lack of lines, cables and distributing substations.

It is very difficult to combat this unfortunate state of affairs, although its evil effects are recognised now, it appears, even by the country's top leaders. But to do anything about it would involve changing the whole structure of the administration, not just of scientific work but of society as a whole, and radical change of that kind is what frightens the conservative Soviet leaders more than anything else. So the authorities carry on issuing resounding instructions and decrees about the 'improvement in the planning of scientific research', the 'raising of the effectiveness of scientific work' and so forth, while the officials continue to do their job, encouraging work on subjects connected with military technology and holding up work on all other subjects. It is not that these officials are inspired with malice or hostility towards the Soviet state; it is simply a matter of common sense. They know that a breakdown in the work of researching into, say a new rocket fuel might cost them their jobs, their whole career or even their heads; but the abandonment of work on the mutagenous action of some chemical preparations on flies could at the very most result in a fatherly reprimand.

Even more catastrophic in its effects is the second of the defects of Soviet scientific work which I have listed—the need to make it fit in with Communist dogmas. The advance of science and progress itself is a continual refutation of all dogmas resting, as is natural, on an earlier and lower level of knowledge. But the dogmas of Marxism-Leninism (a materialist view of the world, progress as a conflict between opposites, the transfer of quantity into quality, the 'negation of negations') belongs entirely to the last century and cannot be brought to embrace such a concept as, for example, the electro-magnetic wave. But it is impossible to speak openly about this in the Soviet Union, with the result that the philosophers have been trying for years to make the idea of radio waves fit into the philosophical concepts of Marxism-Leninism.

The radio wave was, as it happened, fortunate, because it was discovered before the establishment of the Soviet régime in Russia, and it was found to be rather difficult to declare radio non-existent after the event. But subsequent scientific discoveries were declared to be non-existent in the Soviet Union if, in the opinion of those ignorant folk in charge of science, they appeared to be 'incompatible with Marxism-Leninism'.

That was the fate which befell a branch of science with quite respectable antecedents—classical genetics. Everything that had been discovered and written about inherited characteristics and variability in nature, from the experiments of Gregor Mendel to the theory of genes, was declared to be reactionary, bourgeois and strictly forbidden. For belonging to this 'reactionary' school the botanist Nikolai Vavilov was put to prison tortured and paid with his life, professors Levit and

Agol were executed and Professor Sabinin committed suicide. The career in science of thousands of others was ruined, including that of that most able of Soviet geneticists Nikolai Dubinin a remarkable researcher into chemical mutagenes, Josif Rappoport. Instead, from 1931 to 1964 an agronomist from Odessa, Trofim Lysenko, wielded undivided power over Soviet biological science, because his wild theories, unlike those of classical genetics, fitted in perfectly with the teaching of Marxism-Leninism. Lysenko asserted, for example, that in Nature there was not, and could not be, any struggle within any species for existence; that an organism was capable of inheriting characteristics acquired by its parents during their lives, under the influence of its environment; that in certain conditions some types of plants and animals were capable of being turned into others—for example, wheat into rye, or a cuckoo into a chiff-chaff. Lysenko rejected the need for mineral fertilisers in agriculture and forbade the crossing of different kinds of corn and the sowing of certain kinds of beet. Instead he insisted on the 'transformation' of winter wheat into spring wheat and the use of a mixture of soil, turf and manure as a fertiliser. The official insistence, under threat of physical punishment, on the application of Lysenko's theories to Soviet farming led to its disastrous decline.

When in 1948 the science of cybernetics was conceived and began to develop rapidly, in the Soviet Union it was immediately declared to be a 'bourgeois idealist pseudo-science' and was strictly banned. Although the ban was removed in 1956, Soviet computers are still two generations behind Western ones.

At the end of the forties there ceased to appear in Soviet scientific writings any reference to the theory of relativity or to the 'Zionist' Einstein, and in 1951 there even appeared a collection of essays entitled 'Against Idealism in Contemporary Physics' which

169

condemned the 'idealist teachings of Einstein'. Fortunately it did not go so far in the end as a complete rejection of the relativity theory. On the other hand the resonance theory of chemical reactions was for many years rejected entirely and subjected to official anathema.

It is true that today ideological pressure on science and scientists is not carried to such extremes. But it continues just the same and has an extremely painful effect on both. As my work on this book was coming to an end *Pravda* published two hysterical articles one after the other, calling for 'an improvement in the ideological education of scientific personnel'. One of them contained an unambiguous threat addressed to those scientists who, in the author's words, 'flaunt their non-membership of the Party'. *Pravda* accused them of 'turning the other cheek to the enemy'. The idea that there is some 'ideological enemy', assuming different forms in accordance with the demands of the moment ('American imperialism', 'West German irredentism', 'international Zionism') serves as a permanent scarecrow to frighten the whole Soviet population and in particular the scientists.

The ideological pressure is extremely harmful for yet another reason—that it creates an atmosphere of nervousness, squabbling and mutual distrust in scientific establishments. People are not identical in their abilities, and scientific work is precisely one of the spheres in which individual differences reveal themselves especially sharply. A specialist who has turned out to be lacking in the qualities necessary for his branch of science is seldom endowed with sufficient courage or honesty to admit the fact and depart. He will usually attribute his lack of success either to misfortune or— something far more dangerous—to 'the intrigues of the enemy'. In Soviet conditions a mediocre specialist has every possibility of remaining in his job in a

170

scientific establishment and even of taking revenge on his more successful colleagues for their ability. This possibility arises because he can make himself into an authority on the ideology, making 'correct' speeches at Party meetings and other gatherings and throwing suspicion on other abler but less 'ideologically sound' colleagues. With a minimum of skill such a failure in science can quickly make a political career in a scientific establishment, perhaps becoming the Party organiser at an institute and before very long getting appointed to one of the top jobs. Since such a career is always built out of accusations hurled at innocent people—in the overwhelming majority of cases quite fictitious accusations—the atmosphere in an institute which has such an 'ideologue' often becomes quite unbearable. Unfortunately there are generally far more mediocre people than talented ones and there is always a demand for 'ideologues'. And as soon as a squabble starts in an institute or an experimental plant and the most able people start to be persecuted for ideological reasons, all productive scientific work stops even if it was going on previously.

The third defect, which has proved a frightful obstacle to the advance of science in the Soviet Union, is the prevailing conservatism in industry. This affects, of course, the applied sciences in which the result of scientists' efforts has to be realised in practice in the form of technical innovations. They include rocketry, and space research, and I can cite a very striking example of the general resistance to change in this field.

I will say by way of introduction only that the system of centralised planning of industrial production, which none of the half-hearted reforms so far proposed have helped to change, acts as a powerful obstacle to the introduction of anything new in technology. Any reorganisation of a smoothly operating production process means the slowing down or temporary stoppage of production. It involves endless fuss and bother about getting hold of the necessary raw materials, machinery and so forth. What is the point of getting caught up in such unpleasantness? For the sake of winning some doubtful bonuses for being an 'innovator'? Who knows when the 'innovation' will actually be put into practice? Life is much easier if you just carry on producing something you are already familiar with and know how to handle!

That is the way literally all managers of industrial plants in the Soviet Union think privately. Not one of them would on his own initiative start interfering with something which is already working well in order to introduce some improvement, however attractive it may appear. Inventors are most unfortunate people in the Soviet Union. Officially they are supposed to be encouraged, but in practice they are thoroughly disliked, because they are always demanding that their inventions should be introduced into industry. But new methods and ideas are introduced into Soviet factories only as a result of pressure from above, and so long as there is no such pressure any kind of initiative from below discouraged on all sorts of excuses, including public defamation of the character of the inventors and campaigns of slander and victimisation against them.

Industrial managers have more or less the same attitude to new scientific developments. It is, of course, more difficult to reject them than it is to reject the ideas of individual inventors. Nevertheless directors of industrial plants have at their disposal a well-stocked arsenal of devices for obstructing, delaying, requiring further study and so forth. One well-tried method consists in sending a machine which has been developed at one experimental bureau to be examined by another one. There is every chance that the experts at the second bureau will include people sufficiently jealous of the first one to try and cast doubts on the design or practical value of the new machine, irrespective of its real qualities. A correspondence is started up, still more organisations are involved in the affair, and meanwhile the factory carries on turning out its product as before and is saved a lot of trouble.

On 2 September 1956, *Pravda* published an article by me entitled 'What Prevents Inventors from Doing Their Job'. There I quoted astonishing examples of the way the introduction of extremely valuable inventions had been held up. As is the custom, the article was 'discussed' and letters appeared in *Pravda* saying that 'steps had been taken'. But only one of the new developments which I had quoted was actually put into practice a year or two later, and then only because by that time successful prototypes of the same thing had appeared abroad.

The insuperable conservatism of Soviet industry affects, according to the law of feed-back, the applied sciences as well—and not only the applied sciences. Is it really worth while, the scientists ask themselves, making such efforts, using up such physical and nervous energy, if the results of your work will in any case be 'frozen' for ages and will perhaps never be put to practical use? It is a great deal simpler and less troublesome to take over some successful design or principle or technological process from a foreign publication and offer it to industry. Although it is never admitted publicly, foreign technology enjoys great authority in the Soviet Union, and the fact of its being foreign will usually provide an invention with an easier path to actual application in practice. A man is not a prophet in his own country. . .

In this connection there were a series of quite extraordinary events which took place over a period of years in Soviet astronautics.

Werner von Braun versus Yuri Kondratyuk

When in 1961 President Kennedy announced that the Americans were to attempt a landing on the Moon 'in the course of this decade', this had the expected effect in the Soviet Union. Khrushchev demanded to hear the ideas of his scientists about Soviet chances of reaching the Moon. A report on the subject was prepared by Academician Glushko whose name has already appeared in preceding chapters. He described in detail the existing plan for a flight to the Moon, known as the 'Werner von Braun project', which had been drawn up by the well-known German rocket expert, living in the United States, well before the launching of the first sputniks. According to von Braun's project a flight to the Moon required first of all the construction of a large orbital space-station, or platform, which would involve, according to preliminary estimates, putting about seventy power rockets into orbit along with crews and equipment. Once the space-platform had been constructed it would be possible to put the Moon rocket, fuel and the rest on it, assemble the rocket in outer space and then launch it to the Moon.

Glushko gave it as his opinion that this project was the only realistic one, but said it was not capable of realisation in the near future. Indeed, a direct flight to the Moon and back would have required a rocket of gigantic dimensions, with the greater part of its power being expended on penetrating the Earth's atmosphere and overcoming the force of the Earth's gravity. An orbital platform situated outside the Earth's atmosphere would make it possible to reduce the size of the Moon rocket many times.

It is said, that after receiving this report, Khrushchev calmed down somewhat and chose to regard Kennedy's announcement as 'propaganda'. It was doubtful

174

whether even the Americans would be able to carry out von Braun's project in the next decade.

Then there was a clap of thunder. A Moscow engineer, Yuri Khlebtsevich, wrote a letter to the Soviet Academy of Science saying that the Moon could be reached more quickly and more easily by other means. He based his views on a book written by a Russian scientist by the name of Yuri Kondratyuk entitled *The Conquest of Interplanetary Space* and published *in 1929.* Yuri Kondratyuk was born in 1897 and perished in 1942 during the Second World War. In writing his book he borrowed nothing from the 'founder' of Soviet astronautics, Tsiolkovsky, because he knew nothing about Tsiolkovsky. (Nor did anybody else, until, at the beginning of the thirties, Tsiolkovsky was turned into a hero by Soviet propaganda.) Kondratyuk proposed in his book that the best way to reach the Moon would be to put a rocket into orbit round the Moon and then let a small 'excursion cabin' down from that orbit. We know now that in general terms Kondratyuk's ideas coincide with the *Apollo* project which has now been carried out, and it would be very interesting to learn whether the authors of *Apollo* knew anything about Kondratyuk's book.

Glushko replied to Khlebtsevich's letter to the effect that there were all sorts of mad ideas going around and that there was no sense wasting the time of busy people with them. But Khlebtsevich turned out to be a hard nut to crack. A major expert in the field of electronics and the author of many inventions, he had made a serious study of astronautics, astronomy and rocketry. Since he was working in a 'closed' institute, he had access to foreign technical publications and therefore had a good idea of the state of American work on space projects. Having received two or three abrupt refusals from the Academy of Science, all of which came in one way or another from Glushko, he

then came up with another proposal. This time Khlebtsevich proposed sending to the Moon a self-propelled
trolley of modest dimensions but equipped with scientific
instruments. He called his trolley a 'tankette-laboratory'. (It is now called a *lunokhod*, but that does not
alter the essence of the idea.) Khlebtsevich appealed
to the common sense of the academicians, saying that
by refusing to pay attention to Kondratyuk's ideas they
were condemning themselves to certain defeat in the
Moon race with the Americans. They should send at
least a 'tankette-laboratory' to the Moon as soon as
possible. There were already rockets in existence of
sufficient power for that, and in that way, he said, the
Russians would be able to demonstrate their own way
of exploring the Moon, for the time being without the
participation of men, and would thus perform at least
some service for science.

But even this was at the time unacceptable to
Glushko. He had, after all, already informed Khrushchev that the von Braun project was the only possible
one. He had no intention of worrying the men at the
top again, especially if it involved admitting that he
had been wrong in his conclusions and moreover that
some little-known engineer by the name of Khlebtsevich
had found a better way than the top academicians. In
the conservative world of Soviet politics, where everything depends on the authority of officialdom, rational
arguments play a very secondary role. The letter
rejecting his proposal which Khlebtsevich received this
time was extremely abrupt and even threatening in
character. It was suggested quite ambiguously to the
engineer that he would be better advised to mind his
own business and not keep offering unwanted advice.
It was also pointed out that rocketry and space technology constituted a State secret and that the question
would have to be gone into concerning the motives

which moved engineer Khlebtsevich to try and force his way into this secret subject.

However unlikely it may seem in Soviet conditions, Khlebtsevich still did not give up even after this refusal. He began writing articles to newspapers and reviews, some of which were even published in the form of abstract reflections on future developments. Then he himself made a short amateur film about his 'tankette-laboratory' and proceeded to show it in clubs where he delivered lectures on the subject. But at this point the First Section of the Academy of Science (the secret police department which exists in every major Soviet establishment) came into the picture. Khlebtsevich was summoned to the police and warned that he might expect serious unpleasantnesses if he continued to show his film which, it was said, 'misleads the population concerning the prospects of exploring outer space. There was nothing left for Khlebtsevich to do but give up the struggle and return to his own work until such time as he was thrown out of his job.

I met Yuri Sergeyevich Khlebtsevich several times after his 'space epic'. Casting his mind back to what had happened he could only sigh helplessly. He was a man absolutely devoted to his country and, as far as I know, loyal to the Communist régime. I can only imagine what he, as a Russian patriot, felt when he watched the film of Neil Armstrong landing on the Moon.

That was how the conservatism and inflexibility of Soviet applied science led to a strange paradox. The Soviet Union continued in theory to stick to Werner von Braun's ideas of reaching the Moon even after von Braun himself had rejected them and had adopted something very similar to a Russian plan first put forward in 1929!

To this I must add that the entry on Kondratyuk in the Soviet space encyclopaedia of 1969 carefully avoids the question of Kondratyuk's proposed way of getting from the Earth to the Moon. The entry only says vaguely that the scientist considered in his work 'trajectories for space flights involving the minimal expenditure of fuel'. At first sight this is remarkable, because Soviet propagandists usually strive to affirm the 'priority of Soviet science' wherever possible. But your surprise passes when you realise that the editor-in-chief of the encyclopaedia is Professor G. V. Petrovich. This pseudonym conceals none other than Academician Glushko himself!

Nevertheless Khlebtsevich's 'tankette-laboratory' had to be sent to the Moon in the end. Nine years after this 'mistaken' idea had been rejected, the authorities had to return to it simply because something had to be done to offset the magnificent American achievements. I am practically certain, however, that the man who conceived the idea, Khlebtsevich, was not invited to take part in the work.

The Main Weapon

I come finally to the fourth and the most serious defect from which science in the Soviet Union suffers most of all—the preoccupation with secrecy. It is a defect which nevertheless provides the Soviet authorities with their best weapon for deceiving the West.

Every year the Soviet authorities publish a 'List of Matters not to be Revealed in the Press or other Publications'. It is in itself a secret publication, of course, all copies of which are numbered and are distributed for use only to officials of the censorship, editors-in-chief of the most important newspapers and magazines and heads of 'first sections' in secret industrial plants, who are obliged to sign for them. I have not only seen the 'List' on many occasions, but I have read it too, because, being in charge of a department in a popular science magazine, I was constantly in touch

178

with the censors and had to refer to the List with them. It is indeed a large book, since a list of what is secret in the Soviet Union occupies about 300 pages of fine print. It is a very impressive volume, bound in green and embossed with gold.

It is much easier to compile a list of information which is not secret concerning the Soviet Union and its technology and science than to list what is secret. For example, you may refer even in the course of non-classified correspondence or in the press only to a very small number of 'open' factories and research institutes. As for the rest, which means the majority of them, you are not permitted to mention them at all in the press and they have to be referred to in official correspondence as: 'Factory Post-box No.—' or 'Research Institute Post-box No. —'. This way of referring to them has become such a part of everyday practice in the Soviet Union that, if you ask someone where he works he may simply answer: 'In a post-box'—after which it is advisable not to pursue your questions.

However, far from everything about the 'open' factories may be referred to in the press. It is absolutely forbidden, for example, to reveal the daily output of any product. I worked for a time on the factory newspaper of the Moscow motor-car factory which is now named after the Communist Youth League. The factory was then producing, as it still is today, the Moskvich light car. As I have already mentioned, there was a 'secret' section at the factory; but with that exception the plant was entirely open and was even visited by foreigners. Nevertheless the factory newspaper did not have the right to state how many cars were assembled each day. When we told the censors that the annual output of our factory was to be found in Soviet statistical reference books, this had no effect on them. They referred back to their instructions and carried them out. Statistical books were published, they said, under special provisions and what was printed in them could, of course, be copied later, but actually to give our own production figures before they had been passed for publication was quite impossible.

Since the quantity of information in the Soviet Union which is considered secret is so vast there has to be an enormous apparatus for preserving the secrecy. The whole of the Soviet censorship, for example, is known officially as the 'organs of the Committee for the Protection of military and State secrets in the press'. This Committee has its offices in the centre of Moscow, on Kitaisky passage, and even has a sign up at the door. Branches of the Committee operate in all the provincial centres and towns of any size throughout the Soviet Union, while in smaller places the Committee is represented by 'plenipotentiaries'. No printed material—not even the label on a vodka bottle—can be released in the Soviet Union without its first having been passed by the Committee or its agents. For publishing any material which does not bear the censor's stamp of approval the manager of a Soviet printing works can spend eight years in a prison camp.

The Committee's censorship operations extend even to theatrical performances, television programmes, films and public exhibitions. The prominent Soviet biologist Zhores Medvedev recently wrote a book entitled *The Privacy of Correspondence is Protected by Law* in which he proved by means of documents the operation of a postal censorship in the Soviet Union which interferes with private correspondence. His book has not, of course, been published in the Soviet Union, but it has been produced in Britain and it circulates in Russia only in manuscript form.

In spite of all this the Committee deals only with information which is published for general consumption and with material despatched by post. The secrecy of official correspondence, of official exchanges between

180

various departments and of personal conversations is protected by other agencies—belonging to the Committee for State Security, known usually by its initial letters—KGB.

As I have said, every 'post-box' has its own 'first section', staffed by agents of the KGB. This section has a number of functions: it checks up on the 'reliability' of all the employees of the particular plant or office, decides who shall have access to secret information, is responsible for the safe-keeping of secret correspondence, and acts as a registry for the despatch and receipt of secret mail. Apart from its full-time staff, the 'first sections' always have their network of informers among the employees. With their assistance the KGB gets to know who among the employees are the heavy drinkers, which ones are inclined to talk too freely, and so forth. The mildest form of punishment for such people is the immediate blocking of their access to secret information, which means in practice their dismissal from the plant. More often, however, people who talk too much find themselves in prison.

The procedure which has to be gone through before a man can be given access to secret information is long and cumbersome. The person concerned has first to fill in a gigantic questionnaire with dozens of questions concerning not only him but all his relatives as well—his wife, brothers, sisters, parents and his wife's parents. Apart from filling in the questionnaire the applicant has also to write his autobiography, in which he tells his whole life story in chronological order. Then he has to produce character references from his previous place of employment or study, a certificate from the place where he lives, his identity card, a health certificate and a large number of photographs. This pile of paper is handed into the 'first section' which in turn sends the papers off for further checking along with its own recommendation. After a month or so a reply will be received: the person concerned may be employed on secret work on the basis of form No. 1, or on the basis of form No. 2, or he may not have access to secret material of any kind. There can be no appeal against the decision; in fact, nobody knows exactly who took the decision. The person is simply informed in the 'first section' that a decision has been taken. And that's that.

As for the forms referred to—No. 1 or No. 2—they need a little further explanation. The point is that secret information in the Soviet Union is classified into several categories. The least strict of them is known as 'DSP', meaning 'For official use only'. A document bearing the letters DSP may not be published in the press and should not be taken outside the department or plant concerned. The letters DSP are very often used to mark material which contain something which is 'not quite correct' ideologically speaking, as, for example, certain foreign publications, but which does not contain any information about Soviet research work. Occasionally the authorities have reluctantly to allow Soviet scientists to acquaint themselves with the works of foreign specialists, even if their views do not suit the Party ideologists in the Soviet Union. In such a case the book or pamphlet receives a slightly more decorous version of the same stamp—'DNB'— meaning 'For science libraries'.

The next, much larger category of secrecy is indicated by the stamp 'Secret'. Access to material bearing this stamp is permitted only to persons possessing 'Form No. 2', which is the KGB authority to work on secret documents. All documents marked 'Secret' are kept in safes in the 'first section', and every such document has a card made out for it as soon as it is received. On this card is entered the 'primary' information about the document: what it is called, the date it was issued, the author or originator, the number of copies taken from it, the number of pages it consists of, whether it has any other material attached. Subsequently everything that happens to the document is entered on the card, including the names of the people who used it and the dates. This continues until the document is finally handed over to the secret archives or is destroyed or, in very rare cases, it is declassified.

Even more important documents are marked 'Top Secret'—'S.S.' Access to them is open only to people possessing 'Form No. 1'. The rules for handling S.S. documents are naturally even stricter and more time-wasting.

I heard it said by several scientists that there is a special and even higher category of secret classification, but I can say nothing precise about it and do not know even how it is indicated.

To take a secret document outside the establishment to which it belongs, to lose it, or to show it to an unauthorised person without permission from the 'first section' constitutes a criminal offence. Investigations into such cases are carried out by agents of the KGB and the trials take place behind closed doors. Even the judge is not allowed to know the contents of the document which has been lost or shown to someone by the defendant. In passing sentence the court has to content itself with the 'expert' opinion that the document did in fact bear the 'Secret' stamp and contained information constituting a military or State secret. As I have pointed out already, sentences in such cases are always very severe—up to eight years' detention if it was only a matter of a breach of the secrecy rules and there was no suspicion of espionage. In the latter case the most probable sentence would be death.

The passing of secret papers from one place to another and access to them by 'outsiders'—that is, employees of other offices, factories or research institutes, even if they are engaged on secret work—is a very complicated matter. There is, for example, in the Soviet Union a special secret postal service which operates quite separately from the normal post. Secret correspondence is delivered to its destination by armed couriers, known in the Soviet Union as 'feldjager'. They travel round in special vans and carry the mail in sealed briefcases. It stands to reason that the 'special mail', as it is called, is an extremely slow means of communication. No Soviet scientist would think of despatching a secret document by this means simply to keep his colleagues informed about the work he was engaged on. And yet practically all the documents in use at aircraft, radio-electronic and many chemical factories are marked 'Secret' or 'Top Secret'.

The result is that Soviet specialists work in a state of really frightful isolation, not only from the outside world, but from other Soviet industrial plants and research establishments. They simply do not know what their neighbours are doing in spite of the fact that some branches of science have secret departmental magazines which can be read only in working hours and can be obtained only on signing for them in the 'first section'.

The fear of 'giving away' something secret keeps the lips sealed even of those scientists who are working on non-secret subjects. 'The less you talk, the longer you live' is the view of Soviet citizens, who have learnt through experience. Because of this the bogey of secrecy holds up the progress of non-secret scientific work as well. I recall attending a nationwide symposium on cybernetics in Tbilisi at the end of 1965, for example. It was, of course, not a secret meeting, and the themes of all the papers and the basic documents were all carefully selected. Some of the papers delivered there interested me particularly, so I took the text of one of them with me on a trip to the 'Akademgorodok' near Novosibirsk. In the course of a conversation there

184

with members of the staff of the Mathematics Institute of the Siberian branch of the Academy of Science I happened to say that I had been at the Tbilisi symposium and had listened to a lecture on the construction of models of the human memory. The people I was talking to immediately demanded to know whether they could obtain the text of the lecture. I told them I was sure they could, since there was nothing secret about it: all they had to do was to write to the Cybernetics Institute of the Georgian Republic and it would be sent to them. My friends immediately lost interest, saying that it would take six months for them to receive the document. In the end they borrowed the text off me for one night and had it copied by hand. (The Academy's Institute of Mathematics does not possess even the simplest copying machine, because in the Soviet Union such machines are considered to be 'politically dangerous' and are kept under special control only in secret departments.)

What then is the real purpose behind all this fantastic insistence on secrecy? Scientists in the Soviet Union are firmly convinced that the principal objects are: to conceal from the rest of the world the true level reached by science and technology in the Soviet Union, to conceal their own backwardness and at the same time have the possibility of copying without let or hindrance what is new in science and technology in the West without having to pay for it in hard currency. Apart from this, as I hope I have made clear in the course of this book, secrecy makes it easier to hold Western countries to blackmail, by creating the impression of military and technological strength and of real achievement in space research. And finally the traditional secrecy to which everyone in the Soviet Union has become so accustomed makes it possible to avoid or at least lessen the effect of major breakdowns in experimental work.

185

The Last Example

It is sufficient to consider the launchings of the three automatic stations to the Moon—the *Luna* capsules 15, 16 and 17. *Luna-15* was intended, as is now apparent to collect a sample of the Moon's surface at the same time as *Apollo-11* but broke up on landing. Soviet citizens were informed about this launching in rather different terms. First of all there was a communique (a 'TASS statement') saying that 'in accordance with the programme for exploring the Moon *Luna-15* has been launched in the Soviet Union and contact is being maintained with it'. Later it was stated that it had gone into orbit round the Moon. Then, finally, a statement was issued saying that *Luna-15* had 'completed its work'. There was not a word about what *Luna-15* had been supposed to achieve, nor about its crash landing on the Moon. The impression was thus given that everything had gone according to plan.

Exactly the same procedure was adopted for informing the Soviet public (and the rest of the world) about the flight of *Luna-16*. At the beginning the purpose of the launching was given as simply 'further investigation into the Moon'. Then it turned out that some instrument had landed successfully on the Moon, was drilling into its surface and sending back data to the Earth. Finally it was revealed that a module with its samples of Moon dust had set off back to Earth. At this point the Soviet newspapers burst into a chorus of official rejoicing: 'A New Triumph for Soviet Science . . .' and so forth. But at that point not a word was said about the actual size of *Luna-16* or the quantity of Moon dust it had brought back. Only much later, at an international congress in Leningrad, was the size of the sample given—less than four ounces, and then the *Luna-16* was exhibited for inspection. The dimensions of the *lunokhod* were also kept secret for a long time. Secrecy makes everything possible!

186

Nevertheless the harm caused by this excessive secrecy greatly exceeds any advantage that may be derived from it. Apart from the barriers it erects between scientists and the obstacles it puts in the way of exchanging information, the obsession with secrecy adds an incredible amount to the cost of every piece of work that is carried out. On the one hand, scientists have to carry out a great deal of research and development work which in any other country they would take over directly from other firms doing parallel or connected work. On the other hand the whole machinery for maintaining secrecy costs tremendous sums of money to keep going.

Before the *Gemini* programme was embarked on in the United States figures were published of the cost of space research. Among them was an estimate of what it cost to lift each pound of weight into orbit round the Earth. The figure was, I think, slightly more than a hundred dollars. My Soviet scientist friends studied these figures with great interest. They had no idea themselves how much it cost the Soviet Union to put a pound or a kilogram of weight into orbit, and they were quite sure that Korolyov himself did not know either. But their general conclusion was that, if the Americans spent something over a hundred dollars per pound, the figure in the Soviet Union must be at least five times as great.

I am convinced that this was a very cautious estimate. In spite of the fact that people in the Soviet Union earn roughly a fifth of what people earn in the United States, the cost of Soviet space programmes is incomparably higher. The blame for this lies not only in the pursuit of secrecy but also in the low level of technological development requiring that every small part has to be manufactured individually, in the gross inefficiency which flourishes throughout the country, in the chronic thieving which goes on everywhere (even in secret

187

establishments) and in the exceptionally low productivity of labour which is the lowest in Europe.

These are the reasons why we should not be surprised that no Soviet citizens have yet set foot on the Moon. What is surprising is precisely the reverse: the way Korolyov and other talented scientists succeeded in the conditions I have described in making the backward and conservative Soviet Union into a 'space power'.

Irrespective of any political considerations those men are worthy of the deepest admiration of the rest of humanity.

INDEX

Abel, Colonel 153
Academician Korolyov 18
'Akademgorodok' 163, 184
Aldrin 157
Apollo–1 123
Apollo–8 155
Apollo–11 11, 157–8, 186
Apollo–12 11
Apollo–13 11, 158
Apollo–14 11
Apollo–20 158
Apollo programme 10, 150–1, 155–6
Arlazorov, M. 27
Armstrong, Neil 12, 155, 157, 177
Astashenkov, P 58, 105, 130
Atlas rocket 51
Aviation Week 12, 14

Bainkonur 'cosmodrome' 12, 48, 164
Belka and Strelka 84
Belyaev, Pavel 142, 144, 146–7
Beregovoi, Georgi 155
Beria, Lavrenti 161
Birthday, The 17, 21
Blagouravov 19
von Braun, Wernher, 43, 55, 174–5, 177–8
Brezhnev 20, 119, 134, 137, 139
Bykovsky, Valeri 92, 110, 114–6, 149

Carpenter, Malcolm 116
Cooper, Gordon 116
Chalomei 41–2, 46–7, 49, 53, 60, 82, 119, 122
Chistyakova, Tamara 111
Chuvash 92
Cluster Rocket Engine, The 50
Cybernetics Institute of the Georgian Republic 185

Daily Worker 98–100, 102
Dolgov, Peter 89–92

Eisenhower, Dwight 55, 65
Evening News 13
Explorer–1 76
Explorer–3 76

Fairley, Peter 159
Feoktistov, Konstantin 127–8, 130, 135
Fermi, Enrico 163
First Circle, The 32
Flerov, Academician 163
Fuchs, Klaus 153
Fyodorov, V. P. 35–7

Gagarin, Yuri 48, 88, 91, 93–4, 100–2, 105–7, 110, 115, 118, 143, 149
Gallai, Mark 35, 37, 39
Gazenko, Oleg 84
Gemini–1 123
Gemini–3 142
Gemini programme 20–1, 79–80, 123, 139, 149–51, 156, 187
G I R D (group for the study of rocket motors) 23–5, 27–8
Glushko, Academician 46, 49, 59, 78, 174–6, 178
Goddard 23, 26
Golovanov, Yaroslav 88
G P U (secret police) 24
Grissom, Virgil 10, 108, 142
Hitler, Adolf 68

Ilyushin, Sergei 98, 100
Ilyushin, Vladimir 98–9, 102
Institute of Space Medicine 85
Inter-Planetary Ship, An 26
Invisible Man, The 22

Kamanin, General 113
Katushas 29
Keldysh, Mstislav 49, 67, 102, 108
Kennedy, President 174–5
Khariton, Yuri 163
Khlebtsevich, Yuri 175–8
Khlupov 103
Khrushchev, Nikita 15, 19–21, 53–4, 57–8, 67, 72–5, 81–2, 87, 91, 93, 101, 107, 109–10, 117–9, 124–6, 133–7, 139, 141–2, 151, 163, 174
Kleimenov, Ivan 29
Komarov, Vladimir 93, 128, 135, 148, 150
Kondratyuk, Yuri 174–6, 178
Korolyov, Sergei Pavlovitch 15, 17–22, 25–35, 37–47, 49–51, 52–4, 56–61, 67–8, 72–8, 80–4, 86–8, 91–6, 99–101, 105–111, 115–32, 135, 138–41, 143–8, 151, 153–6, 160, 187–8
Kostikov, A. G. 29
Kosygin 20, 119, 134, 137, 139
Krogers, The 153
Kroshkin, Mikhail Galaktionovich 103–5, 112, 131

Langemak, Georgi 29–30
Lavrentiev, Mikhail 163
Lebedev 73–4, 162
Leipunsky, Academician 163
Lenin 40

189

Leningrad Laboratory of Gas Dynamics (GLD) 28
Leonov, Alexei 92, 138, 140, 142–6
Likarenko, Colonel 38–9
Lonsdale, Gordon 153
Luna–1 77
Luna–2 160
Luna–15 157–8, 186
Luna–16 157, 159, 186
Luna–17 159–60, 186
Lunik 11
Lunokhod 150, 158–60, 186
Lysenko, Trofim 169

Mao Tse-tung 101
Markusha, Anatoli 17, 21, 38
Medvedev, R. 156
Medvedev, Zhores 180
Men Who Forge the Thunder, The 88
Mendel, Gregor 168
Mercury space-craft 81, 115–6
Midas satellites 109
Mikoyan, Anastas Ivanovich 136
Moscow magazine 26, 127
Moskvich motor car 65–6

Nesmeyanov, A. N. 97, 102
Nikolayev 92, 110–13, 116, 149, 156
N K V D (secret police) 31
Novosti press agency 106
Novy Mir (No. 4 for 1963) 35

Oberth 23, 26
Ogden, Dennis 98–9, 102
Ozerov, Prof. G. A. 146

Parin, Vasili 84
Pcholka and Mushka 86
Perelman, J. L. 27
Petrovich, Professor G. V. 49, 178
Pioneer–4 76–7
Pontecorvo, Bruno 153, 163
Popovich 92, 110–12, 116, 149
Powers, Gary 66
Pravda 22, 170, 173
Privacy of Correspondence is Protected by Law, The 180

Ramzin, Professor Leonid 33, 40
Rappoport, Josif 169
RD-107 cluster rocket engines 77–9
RD-108 79
Research into inter-planetary space by means of Jet Power 26
Rocket Motors 22
Rosenbergs, The 153
Ryabchikov, Yevgeni 106

Sabinin, Professor 169
Sakharov, Andrei 156, 162
Salyut space station 12–14
Saturn–5 51

Saturn rocket 123
Schirra, Walter 116
Sedov, L. I. 19
Sevestyanov 156
Shumsky, Professor 33
Sidewinder rocket, 153
Solzhenitsyn, Alexander 32
Soviet Academy of Science 49, 67, 84–5, 175–7
Soviet Encyclopedia of Space Flight 74
Soyuz–1 148
Soyuz–4 155
Soyuz–5 155
Soyuz–10 12, 14
Soyuz space-craft 121–3, 131, 139, 147, 155–6
Stalin 30, 40, 43, 53, 72, 75

Tereshkova, Valentina 110–11, 113–116, 149
Technology and Life 26
Tested in the Sky 35, 38
Times, The 12, 14, 156
Titan–2 79–80
Titov, German 91, 93, 109–10
Triolovsky, Konstantin 26–7
TU–2 dive-bomber 31
Tukhachevsky, Mikhail 25, 30
Tupolev, Andrei 31, 146
Turchin, V. 156

V–1 rockets 44
Vanguard–1 76
Vanguard satellite 55
Vavilov, Nikolai 168
Voronin 75, 83, 85, 89, 129
Vasilchenko 35
Vekslev, Academician 163
Voskhod series 80, 106, 127–8, 131–3, 136–9, 140
Voskhod–1 104, 148–9
Voskhod–2 141–2, 144–8
Voskresensky, L. A. 34, 42, 49, 59, 68, 80, 95, 117–8, 121–4, 132, 139–41, 160
Vostok space-craft 80, 93, 100–101, 108–9, 111, 113, 115–6, 120–2, 126, 128–9, 131–3, 143
Vostok–2 108–9, 140
Vostok–3 136

Wells, H. G. 22

Yangel 43, 47, 49, 53, 82, 122
Yegorov, Dr Boris 128, 135, 139
Yunganov, Victor 44–5
Yunost magazine 88

Zander, Freidrich 23, 26, 153
Znaniye-Sila 133
Zond–6 space station 159
Zond–7 159